Physical Inorganic Chemistry

THE PHYSICAL INORGANIC CHEMISTRY SERIES

Robert A. Plane and Michell J. Sienko, Editors

Physical Inorganic Chemistry	*M. J. Sienko and R. A. Plane (Cornell)*
Boron Hydrides	*W. N. Lipscomb (Harvard)*
Metal Ions in Aqueous Solution	*J. P. Hunt (Washington State)*

sienko—plane

CORNELL UNIVERSITY

PHYSICAL INORGANIC CHEMISTRY

W. A. BENJAMIN, INC.

1963 *new york amsterdam*

PHYSICAL INORGANIC CHEMISTRY

Library of Congress Catalog Card Number: 63–15825
Manufactured in the United States of America

The manuscript was received on November 28, 1962, and this volume was published on May 6, 1963

The publisher is pleased to acknowledge the assistance of Russell F. Peterson, who produced the illustrations, and William Prokos, who designed the cover and dust jacket

W. A. BENJAMIN, INC.
2465 Broadway, New York 25, New York

Editors' Foreword

In recent years few fields of chemistry have expanded at a rate to match that of inorganic chemistry. Aside from the stimulus afforded by the demand for new materials, a primary cause for the resurgence has been the application of physics and physical chemistry concepts to inorganic problems. As a result, both researchers active in the field and students entering the field need to become as thoroughly familiar with physical concepts as with descriptive information. However, there is presently no single point of view sufficiently general to organize the entire discipline. Instead, various points of view have arisen corresponding to the most powerful methods of attack in each research area. The synthesis of these different points of view constitutes the present series of monographs. Each monograph is contributed by an inorganic chemist active in a particular research area and reflects the methods of approach characteristic to that area. The operational procedure has been to invite able scientists to write where their interests lead them.

The series fulfills several functions. Through flexible selection of several of the monographs to supplement the introductory volume, it can be used as a textbook for an advanced inorganic chemistry course that makes full use of physical chemistry prerequisites. As a series in total, it is a reference treatise of inorganic chemistry systematized by physical principles. Finally, each monograph by itself represents a specialist's introduction to a specific research field.

It is hoped that the authors contributing to this series have succeeded in directing attention to unsolved problems and that their efforts will be repaid by continued research advances in inorganic chemistry.

M. J. Sienko
R. A. Plane

Ithaca, New York
February 1963

Preface

This monograph introduces the basic principles of present-day inorganic chemistry. Because current research in the field is strongly oriented by the application of physical methods, appreciation of the inorganic research literature demands a working knowledge of the concepts of physics and physical chemistry. In this book, attention is directed to the use of these concepts in five areas basic to inorganic chemistry: atomic structure, molecules, solid state, liquids and solutions, and chemical reactions. Each of these areas, outlined in a separate chapter of this book, is expanded in one or more of the succeeding monographs of the series. It is our hope that in using the physical inorganic series as a text the individual instructor will expand coverage of those basic topics having special interest for him by addition of the other volumes that develop an expert's more searching analysis. In this way the student will receive not only a stimulating introduction to graduate research but also a discriminating summary of descriptive facts. It is assumed that the reader is familiar with the calculus, elementary physics, and introductory physical chemistry. In fact, the major purpose of this volume is to serve as a bridge between these disciplines and inorganic chemistry.

M. J. Sienko
R. A. Plane

Ithaca, New York
February 1963

Contents

Introduction

Concepts from Thermodynamics

The field of inorganic chemistry can be organized around a number of unifying concepts. These include: the periodic table of the elements; the structure of atoms, molecules, and materials; the nature of the bonding; the reaction kinetics and mechanisms. However, the most powerful approach to inorganic chemistry as to any physical science is that of thermodynamics. Its power derives from the fact that it is applicable to all systems no matter what their structure, bonding, kinetic aspects, etc. In certain cases, perhaps less numerous than for organic chemistry, the course of inorganic reaction may be kinetically controlled, but even here the kinetic details must be consistent with thermodynamic requirements on the system.

As a common basis for the following discussions of structure, bonding, and chemical reactions these thermodynamic parameters and relations will prove useful:

Energy, usually designated as E or U. Its sign convention is such that the energy of the system is increased by work done on the system. Thus, $\Delta E = Q - W$, where ΔE is the increase in energy of the system, Q is the heat absorbed by the system, and W is work done by the system. On a particle scale—e.g., per atom—differences in energy are usually expressed in electron volts (1 ev = 1.60×10^{-12} erg) or wave numbers (1 cm^{-1} = 1.99×10^{-16} erg). On a macroscopic scale, energy changes are usually expressed as kilocalories (1 kcal = 4.186×10^{10} ergs, or 1 ev per particle is the equivalent of 23.066 kcal per mole).

Enthalpy, or heat content, usually designated as H. Enthalpy is defined as the sum of the energy and the pressure-volume product, $H = E + PV$. For a system undergoing change at constant pressure, ΔH equals $\Delta E + P\,\Delta V$—that is, the change in enthalpy is equal to the change in energy plus the work done on the surroundings. In other words, if heat is added to a system at constant pressure, the heat absorbed by the system is equal to the enthalpy increase and is used partially to raise the energy and partially to do work on the surroundings. The units for enthalpy are the same as for energy.

Entropy, usually designated as S. On a phenomenological basis, entropy represents the isothermally unavailable energy per degree temperature (unavailable in the sense that it cannot be converted to work at constant temperature); thus $\Delta E - T\,\Delta S$ represents available energy. Perhaps more physical insight is gained from the statistical interpretation of entropy as a measurement of the degree of randomness or probability of the system. In the Boltzmann definition $S = k \ln w$, where w is the number of independent arrangements possible for the particles of the system at fixed E and V (k is the Boltzmann constant, 1.38×10^{-16} erg per degree). The usual molar units for entropy are calories per degree per mole, sometimes referred to as "entropy units." The criterion for any spontaneous change is that the total entropy (system plus surroundings) must increase. However, as noted below, a more common criterion for spontaneous change ignores the surroundings, in which case both entropy and energy must be considered.

Free energy, also referred to as the Gibbs free energy, usually represented as F, or G. The free energy is defined by $F = E + PV - TS = H - TS$. At constant temperature and pressure, $\Delta F = \Delta E + P\,\Delta V - T\,\Delta S$—that is, the increase in free energy is equal to the increase in energy plus the work done on the surroundings less the change in energy unavailable as work. Under these conditions of constant pressure and temperature, the criterion for spontaneous change of a system is that its free energy decrease. Thus under usual chemical conditions equilibrium is established when the free energy reaches a minimum. The units for free energy are generally kilocalories.

Chemical potential, generally designated as μ or $\overline{F}$. For a mixture of components, the total free energy is given by $F = \Sigma n_i\mu_i$, where n_i is the number of moles of component i in the mixture and μ_i is the change of total free energy with respect to addition of component i—i.e., $\mu_i = (\partial F/\partial n_i)_{P,T,n_j,\ldots}$. Because F depends on the amount of material (is an extensive property), whereas μ does not (is intensive), it is the chemical potential that is more generally useful. The units of chemical potential are kilocalories per mole.

Standard states. Because thermodynamic parameters generally are a function of pressure, temperature, and concentration, it is necessary for comparison reasons to select and specify reference states. The reference states are arbitrary and change from system to system as convenient. Usually, standard pressure means 1 atm. Standard temperature may be 0°K, 0°C, or 25°C and therefore needs to be specified. However, the major compilations of inorganic data, such as the National Bureau of Standards (N.B.S.) tables or Latimer's oxidation potentials are referred to 25°C. The real problem is the standard state for concentration, especially in aqueous solution. A wide variety are in use. For example, one might choose unit mole fraction—i.e., the pure substance. Alternatively, one might refer to a saturated solution. Perhaps the most common is the dilute-solution, hypothetical state. This hypothetical standard state is an ideal 1 molal solution, where "ideal" is defined as having the same rate of change of μ with molality as occurs in the infinitely dilute solution.

Activity. The dependence of μ on concentration is generally embodied in $\mu = \mu_0 + RT \ln a$, where μ_0 is the chemical potential of the standard state and a is called the activity. For solutions, the activity is generally expressed as a product of an activity coefficient, γ, and the molality, m. Obviously, in the standard state $\mu = \mu_0$, so $a = 1$. In an infinitely dilution solution, m and a become equal—i.e., γ becomes one. However, this cannot be the standard state, since a has become zero. Instead, the standard state is a hypothetical, ideal solution in which $\gamma = 1$ when $m = 1$, thus making $a = 1$. Activity is a unit-less quantity, but activity coefficient has units of reciprocal concentration.

Equilibrium constant. At equilibrium for any chemical reaction at constant temperature and pressure the change in chemical potential is equal to zero, $\Delta\mu = 0 = \Delta\mu_0 + RT \ln (a_{\text{products}}/a_{\text{reactants}})$. In this expression a_{products} is the result of multiplying together the activities of all components formed in the reaction raised to their appropriate powers as given by the coefficients in the balanced equation, and

$a_{\text{reactants}}$ is the corresponding term for the reactants. Since $\Delta\mu_0$ is a constant and equal to $-RT \ln (a_{\text{products}}/a_{\text{reactants}})$ at equilibrium, it follows that the activity ratio must also be a constant at constant temperature and pressure. This activity ratio is the equilibrium constant, generally designated by K. It has no units and is independent of concentration. In practice one often measures concentrations as opposed to activities, so that equilibrium quotients, or apparent equilibrium constants, do depend on concentration. If, however, these apparent K's are extrapolated to infinite dilution (all γ's equal one), the true equilibrium constant is obtained.

Heats of reaction. From the definition of free energy as $F = H - TS$ it follows that in the standard state, usually designated by a superscript or a subscript zero, the isothermal change in free energy for conversion of reactants to products is $\Delta F^\circ = \Delta H^\circ - T\,\Delta S^\circ = -RT \ln K$. It is easily shown that $(d \ln K)/dT = \Delta H^\circ/RT^2$. Thus by measuring equilibrium constants at various temperatures it is possible to determine ΔH° for the reaction. Once ΔF° and ΔH° have been thus found, ΔS° can be calculated. It is important that these two components, ΔH° and ΔS°, be separately evaluated before making assertions as to importance of energy (hence, structure and bonding) and entropy (configuration change) in controlling the direction of chemical change.

1

Atomic Structure

In chemistry an atom may be approximated as a collection of positive and negative charges. The positive charges and nearly all the mass are concentrated in the nuclear region, which has negligibly small dimensions (the order of a few fermi units; 1 fermi = 10^{-13} cm) compared to the over-all dimensions attributed to the atom. The negatively charged region, with a radius some 10^5 times as large as the nucleus, is the principal concern of chemistry.

• 1-1 One-Electron Wave Functions

The description of the atom's electronic region has long been a problem because of the reluctance to abandon physical models having macroscopic analogs. Yet, the uncertainty principle, by limiting the extent of visualization permitted, requires that the electronic description be in more abstract language. The way this is now done is in terms of a wave-mechanical model in which a sufficiently complete description of electrons is given by their wave functions. Wave functions are solutions of the Schrödinger wave equation

$$\frac{\partial^2\psi}{\partial x^2} + \frac{\partial^2\psi}{\partial y^2} + \frac{\partial^2\psi}{\partial z^2} + \frac{8\pi^2 m}{h^2}(E - V)\psi = 0 \qquad (1)$$

where ψ is the wave function, h is Planck's constant, m is the mass of the electron, E is its energy, and V represents the potential in which the electron is found. This equation, which is here given in Cartesian coordinates for the case of a single electron, can be deduced by introducing the deBroglie condition,

$$\lambda = \frac{h}{p} \tag{2}$$

(relating the wavelength λ of a particle to its momentum p) into the general equation for standing waves. The general equation for wave motion is

$$\frac{\partial^2 A}{\partial q^2} = \frac{1}{v^2}\frac{\partial^2 A}{\partial t^2} \tag{3}$$

where A is the amplitude of the wave, q is a general coordinate, v is the wave velocity (or phase velocity), and t is the time. If it is assumed that the wave is sinusoidal, then

$$A = \psi e^{-2\pi i\nu t} \tag{4}$$

where ψ is the amplitude, dependent on coordinate only, and ν is the frequency of the wave. Differentiation of Equation (*4*) twice with respect to the coordinate gives

$$\frac{\partial^2 A}{\partial q^2} = \frac{\partial^2 \psi}{\partial q^2} e^{-2\pi i\nu t} \tag{5}$$

and twice with respect to time

$$\frac{\partial^2 A}{\partial t^2} = -4\pi^2\nu^2\psi e^{-2\pi i\nu t} \tag{6}$$

Substitution in Equation (*3*) gives

$$\frac{\partial^2 \psi}{\partial q^2} = \frac{-4\pi^2\nu^2\psi}{v^2} \tag{7}$$

which is the time-independent general equation for standing waves.

Since $v = \nu\lambda$ and λ is given by Equation (*2*), we can rewrite (*7*) as follows:

$$\frac{\partial^2\psi}{\partial q^2} = \frac{-4\pi^2 p^2 \psi}{h^2} \tag{8}$$

Since

$$\frac{p^2}{2m} = E - V \tag{9}$$

where $p^2/2m$ is the kinetic energy of the electron, E is its total energy, and V is its potential energy, Equation (*8*) can be rewritten

$$\frac{\partial^2\psi}{\partial q^2} = \frac{-8\pi^2 m(E - V)\psi}{h^2} \tag{10}$$

as the Schrödinger time-independent equation in one dimension. In Cartesian coordinates the equation is usually written as in Equation (*1*); in spherical polar coordinates, it has the form

$$\frac{\partial}{\partial r}\left(r^2 \frac{\partial\psi}{\partial r}\right) + \frac{1}{\sin\theta}\frac{\partial}{\partial\theta}\left(\sin\theta\frac{\partial\psi}{\partial\theta}\right) + \frac{1}{\sin^2\theta}\frac{\partial^2\psi}{\partial\phi^2} + \frac{8\pi^2 mr^2}{h^2}(E - V)\psi = 0 \tag{11}$$

where r is the radial distance from the center of the force field, ϕ is the azimuthal angle—that is, the longitude angle or the angular deviation from the xz plane—and θ is the polar angle, or the angular deviation from the z direction.

The wave functions ψ, which are solutions of the wave equation, are related to the electron probability distribution. However, whereas a probability function can only be real and positive, ψ is generally complex (i.e., has real plus imaginary terms) and may be negative. It is assumed that ψ multiplied by its complex conjugate (which is the same mathematical function but has each i replaced by $-i$) gives directly the electron probability density. Thus the probability P of finding an electron in the volume element $d\tau$ is given by

$$P = \psi\psi^* \, d\tau \tag{12}$$

where ψ^* is the complex conjugate of the wave function ψ.

For the case of a one-electron atom in which the electron has a potential energy

$$V = -\frac{Ze^2}{r} \tag{13}$$

where Z is the positive charge of the nucleus, the solutions of the wave equation *(11)* are found to be of the form

$$\psi_{nlm} = -Ce^{-Zr/na_0}\left(\frac{2Zr}{na_0}\right)^l L_{n+l}^{2l+1}\left(\frac{2Zr}{na_0}\right) P_l^{|m|}(\cos\theta)e^{im\phi} \tag{14}$$

ψ_{nlm} represents a particular solution of the wave equation for designated values of the three quantum numbers n, l, and m. n is the principal quantum number and has integral values 1, 2, 3, . . ., corresponding respectively to the K-level, L-level, M-level . . . of X-ray spectroscopy. The second quantum number l is often called the orbital quantum number; for a given n, l can be 0, 1, 2, 3, . . ., $n - 1$, corresponding to designations s, p, d, f, . . ., respectively. The third quantum number m, called the magnetic quantum number because it relates to orientation of electron motion with respect to an external field, for a given n and l, can have values 0, ±1, ±2, . . ., $\pm l$. (Any one-electron wave function can be used to describe an electron distribution and, hence, is frequently referred to as an *atomic orbital*.)

C is a constant of normalization which ensures that the total probability of finding a given electron is unity. Its value is

$$\left\{\frac{Z^3(2l+1)(l-|m|)!(n-l-1)!}{\pi(na_0)^3(l+|m|)!n[(n+l)!]^3}\right\}^{1/2}$$

a_0, called the Bohr radius and having a value of 0.53 A, is simply a convenient unit for measuring atomic distances. It corresponds to the radius of the first orbit in the Bohr model of the hydrogen atom.

The designation $L_{n+l}^{2l+1}(2Zr/na_0)$ stands for a function called the associated Laguerre polynomial. It has the form

$$L_{n+l}^{2l+1}\left(\frac{2Zr}{na_0}\right) = \sum_{k=0}^{n-l-1}(-1)^{k+1} \times \frac{[(n+l)!]^2}{(n-l-1-k)!(2l+1+k)!k!}\left(\frac{2Zr}{na_0}\right)^k \tag{15}$$

where k is a summation index running over integral values from zero to the particular value of $n - l - 1$.

The designation $P_l^{|m|}(\cos\theta)$ represents a function of the angle θ. It is called the associated Legendre polynomial and is

$$P_l^{|m|}(\cos\theta) = \frac{(1-\cos^2\theta)^{|m|/2}}{2^l l!}\frac{d^{l+|m|}}{d\cos\theta^{l+|m|}}(\cos^2\theta - 1)^l$$

The solutions for the various combinations of quantum numbers commonly encountered are given in Table 1-1. The wave functions for

Table 1-1 *Wave functions ψ_{nlm} for one-electron atom*

1*s*	$\psi_{100} = \frac{1}{\sqrt{\pi}}\left(\frac{Z}{a_0}\right)^{3/2} e^{-Zr/a_0}$
2*s*	$\psi_{200} = \frac{1}{4\sqrt{2\pi}}\left(\frac{Z}{a_0}\right)^{3/2}\left(2 - \frac{Zr}{a_0}\right) e^{-Zr/2a_0}$
2*p*	$\psi_{210} = \frac{1}{4\sqrt{2\pi}}\left(\frac{Z}{a_0}\right)^{5/2} e^{-Zr/2a_0} r\cos\theta$
	$\psi_{21(\pm1)} = \frac{1}{8\sqrt{\pi}}\left(\frac{Z}{a_0}\right)^{5/2} e^{-Zr/2a_0} r\sin\theta\, e^{\pm i\phi}$
3*s*	$\psi_{300} = \frac{1}{81\sqrt{3\pi}}\left(\frac{Z}{a_0}\right)^{3/2}\left(27 - \frac{18Zr}{a_0} + \frac{2Z^2r^2}{a_0^2}\right) e^{-Zr/3a_0}$
3*p*	$\psi_{310} = \frac{\sqrt{2}}{81\sqrt{\pi}}\left(\frac{Z}{a_0}\right)^{5/2}\left(6r - \frac{Zr^2}{a_0}\right) e^{-Zr/3a_0}\cos\theta$
	$\psi_{31(\pm1)} = \frac{1}{81\sqrt{\pi}}\left(\frac{Z}{a_0}\right)^{5/2}\left(6r - \frac{Zr^2}{a_0}\right) e^{-Zr/3a_0}\sin\theta\, e^{\pm i\phi}$
3*d*	$\psi_{320} = \frac{1}{81\sqrt{6\pi}}\left(\frac{Z}{a_0}\right)^{7/2} r^2 e^{-Zr/3a_0}(3\cos^2\theta - 1)$
	$\psi_{32(\pm1)} = \frac{1}{81\sqrt{\pi}}\left(\frac{Z}{a_0}\right)^{7/2} r^2 e^{-Zr/3a_0}\sin\theta\cos\theta\, e^{\pm i\phi}$
	$\psi_{32(\pm2)} = \frac{1}{162\sqrt{\pi}}\left(\frac{Z}{a_0}\right)^{7/2} r^2 e^{-Zr/3a_0}\sin^2\theta\, e^{\pm 2i\phi}$

the 1*s*, 2*s*, 3*s*, etc., distributions are spherically symmetrical about the nucleus, since they show no dependence on the angles θ and ϕ—that is, these wave functions vary only with the radial distance r. The other wave functions—2*p*, 3*p*, 3*d*—have both radial and angular dependences, which for simplicity are usually considered separately. Figure 1-1 shows the radial dependence, ψ_r, of each of the wave functions of Table 1-1 and also the radial dependence of the total probability of finding the electron in a spherical shell of radius r and thickness dr. Since ψ_r^2 gives a probability per unit volume, multiplication by $4\pi r^2\,dr$ gives the probability per spherical shell. As can be seen from Table 1-1, the wave functions ψ_{200}, ψ_{300}, ψ_{310}, and $\psi_{31(\pm 1)}$ have parenthetical terms which can equal zero at finite values of r. This means that the wave function goes through zero at definite values of r. This in turn is reflected in a zero probability, or a so-called node, in the radial distribution function. Thus, for example, the probability function for the 2*s* distribution consists of a sphere within a spherical shell. For any distribution the number of radial nodes is $n - l - 1$.

For understanding the stereo aspects of chemistry, it is the angular part of the wave function that is of primary interest. Let us consider first the angular dependence of the *p* functions. For a given principal quantum number n, one of the *p* functions is real and shows no dependence on the longitudinal angle ϕ. For example, ψ_{210} is symmetrical about the z axis. This is in general true for any function having magnetic quantum number $m = 0$. However, the other *p* functions, $m = \pm 1$, depend on ϕ and furthermore are complex (part real and part imaginary). Conventionally, these complex functions are replaced by different *p* functions which are formed by linear combinations of the complex ones. Thus, to get the ϕ dependence for the new, real *p* functions we can, by using the relations

$$e^{i\phi} = \cos\phi + i\sin\phi$$

$$e^{-i\phi} = \cos\phi - i\sin\phi$$

take the linear combinations

$$e^{i\phi} + e^{-i\phi} = 2\cos\phi$$

$$e^{i\phi} - e^{-i\phi} = 2i\sin\phi$$

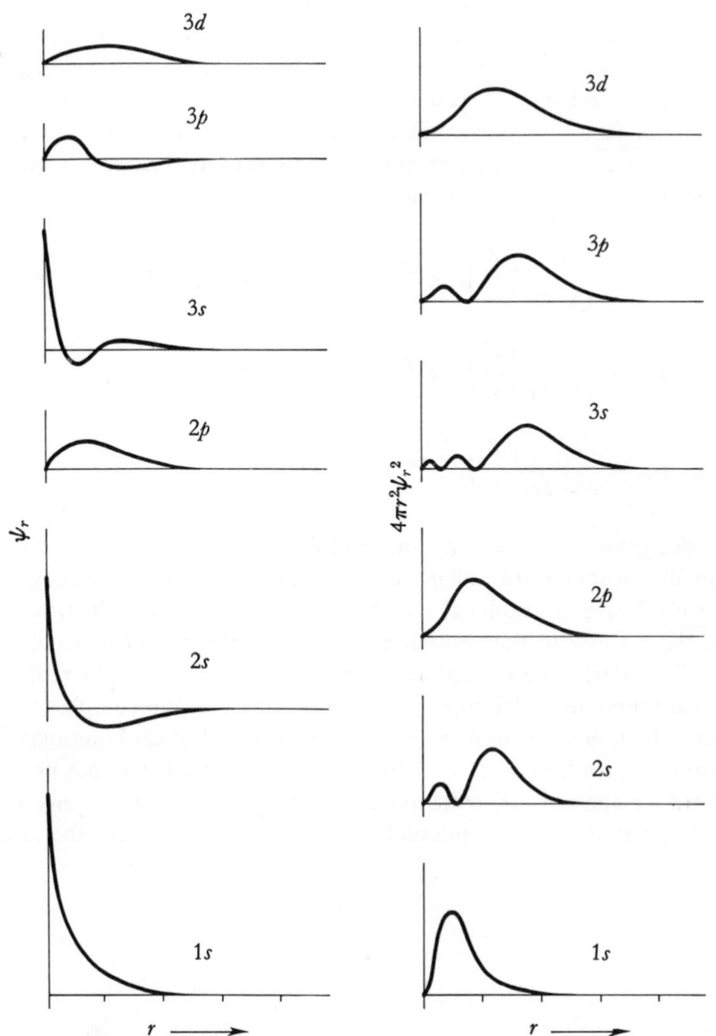

Figure 1-1 *Radial distribution functions for one-electron atom. Dashed lines show radial wave functions; solid lines, the radial distribution function,* $4\pi r^2\psi^2_r$.

which amounts to combining two waves running in opposite directions around the z axis into two standing waves, concentrated respectively along the x and the y directions. Again it is necessary to introduce a numerical factor of normalization, so that after squaring the wave function, the total probability comes out to be unity. After this is done, the real wave functions become

$$\psi_{p_x} = \frac{1}{4\sqrt{2\pi}}\left(\frac{Z}{a_0}\right)^{5/2} e^{-Zr/2a_0} r \sin\theta\cos\phi$$

$$\psi_{p_y} = \frac{1}{4\sqrt{2\pi}}\left(\frac{Z}{a_0}\right)^{5/2} e^{-Zr/2a_0} r \sin\theta\sin\phi$$

$$\psi_{p_z} = \frac{1}{4\sqrt{2\pi}}\left(\frac{Z}{a_0}\right)^{5/2} e^{-Zr/2a_0} r \cos\theta$$

The designations ψ_{p_x}, ψ_{p_y}, ψ_{p_z} indicate that the angular factors concentrate the probabilities along the x, y, and z directions, respectively. Figure 1-2 gives a graphical representation of the angular distribution. The signs apply to the wave function within the region labeled.

Similarly, the d functions given in Table 1-1 are usually replaced by real functions which are linear combinations of the complex forms given. It should be emphasized that the choice of linear combinations is arbitrary, and, in fact, a set useful for one purpose may not be convenient for another. For the majority of compounds where d electrons are important—e.g., compounds of transition elements—the atom

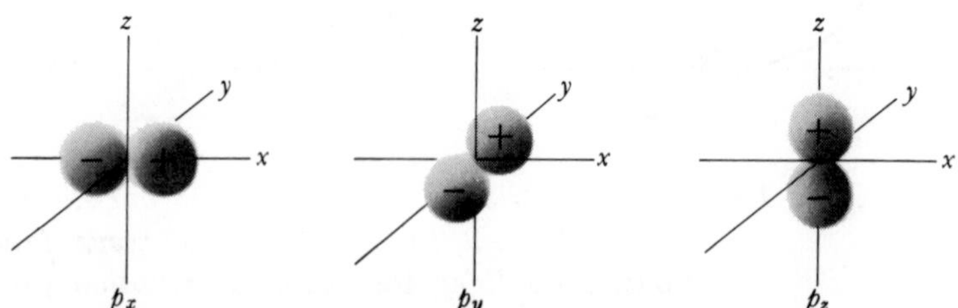

Figure 1-2 *Representation of the angular distribution probability for p_x, p_y, p_z (sign of the wave function shown).*

with d electrons is located in a field of cubic symmetry. Cubic symmetry may be produced by having the surrounding atoms at the corners of an octahedron. For cubic symmetry, the following linear combinations are most convenient:

$$\psi_{d_{z^2}} = \psi_{d(m=0)}$$

$$\psi_{d_{x^2-y^2}} = \frac{1}{\sqrt{2}}\left(\psi_{d(m=+2)} + \psi_{d(m=-2)}\right)$$

$$\psi_{d_{xy}} = -\frac{i}{\sqrt{2}}\left(\psi_{d(m=+2)} - \psi_{d(m=-2)}\right)$$

$$\psi_{d_{yz}} = -\frac{i}{\sqrt{2}}\left(\psi_{d(m=+1)} - \psi_{d(m=-1)}\right)$$

$$\psi_{d_{zx}} = \frac{1}{\sqrt{2}}\left(\psi_{d(m=+1)} + \psi_{d(m=-1)}\right)$$

In real form, the $3d$ wave functions are

$$\psi_{d_{z^2}} = \frac{1}{81\sqrt{6\pi}}\left(\frac{Z}{a_0}\right)^{7/2} r^2 e^{-Zr/3a_0}(3\cos^2\theta - 1)$$

$$\psi_{d_{x^2-y^2}} = \frac{1}{81\sqrt{2\pi}}\left(\frac{Z}{a_0}\right)^{7/2} r^2 e^{-Zr/3a_0}\sin^2\theta\cos 2\phi$$

$$\psi_{d_{xy}} = \frac{1}{81\sqrt{2\pi}}\left(\frac{Z}{a_0}\right)^{7/2} r^2 e^{-Zr/3a_0}\sin^2\theta\sin 2\phi$$

$$\psi_{d_{yz}} = \frac{\sqrt{2}}{81\sqrt{\pi}}\left(\frac{Z}{a_0}\right)^{7/2} r^2 e^{-Zr/3a_0}\sin\theta\cos\theta\sin\phi$$

$$\psi_{d_{zx}} = \frac{\sqrt{2}}{81\sqrt{\pi}}\left(\frac{Z}{a_0}\right)^{7/2} r^2 e^{-Zr/3a_0}\sin\theta\cos\theta\cos\phi$$

The electronic distribution described by the wave function $\psi_{d_{z^2}}$ has its maximum value along the z axis; $d_{x^2-y^2}$, along the x and y axes; $\psi_{d_{xy}}$, $\psi_{d_{yz}}$, $\psi_{d_{zx}}$, along lines 45° to the axes in the xy, yz, and zx planes, respec-

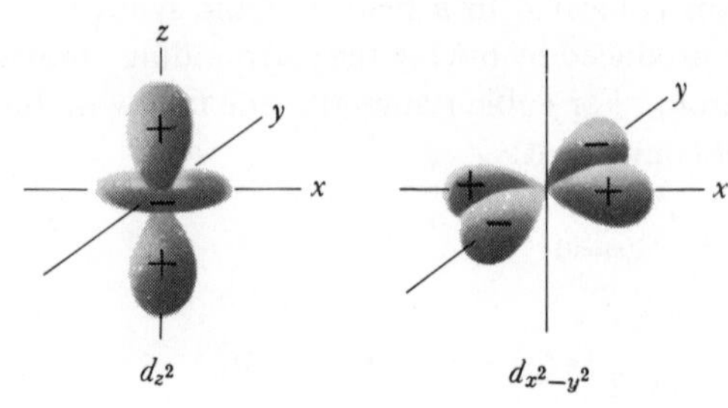

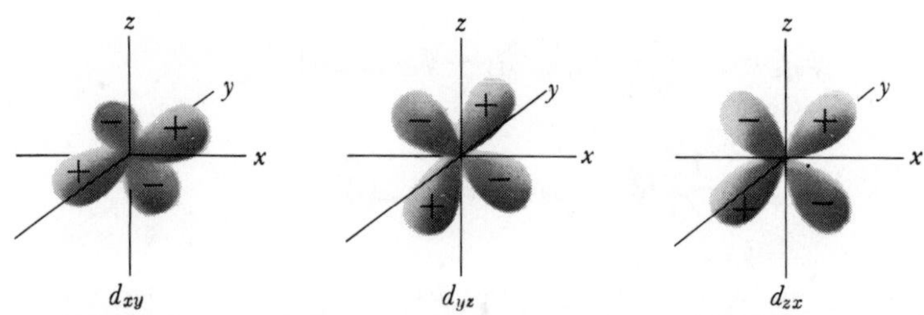

Figure 1-3 *Representation of the angular distribution probability for d_{z^2}, $d_{x^2-y^2}$, d_{xy}, d_{zx}, d_{yz} (sign of wave function shown).*

tively. Graphical representations of the angular dependence of the probability distributions are given in Figure 1-3. The algebraic signs indicate the sign of the wave function in that portion of space so labeled.

• 1-2 Many-Electron Atoms

The above wave functions, being valid for hydrogen-like atoms consisting of nuclear charge Z and a single electron, are not sufficient to describe atoms containing more than one electron. The exact problem cannot be solved because of the difficulty of taking into account the influence of each electron on all the other electrons in the atom. Approximate methods are available, the best of which is the Hartree-Fock method. In this method each electron is assumed to move in an average field arising from the nucleus and all the other electrons. To obtain the appropriate wave function a first guess is made as to the average field in which each electron moves. The resultant wave functions are then used to recalculate the field for a particular electron. The result of that calculation is fed back to improve the field calculation. By successive approximations a result is finally obtained which is said to be "self-consistent" in the sense that each wave function can be calculated by using the wave functions of the other electrons.

An alternate approximation is the Slater method of shielding constants. The method assumes that the wave function is of the form

$$Cr^{(n^*-1)} \exp\left[-\frac{(Z-\sigma)r}{n^*a_0}\right] X(\theta,\phi)$$

where X represents the angular part, which in general is not critical in determining the energy. n^* is the effective principal quantum number and has the values 1, 2, 3, 3.7, 4.0, 4.2 for n = 1, 2, 3, 4, 5, 6, respectively. σ is a shielding constant selected according to the following rules ("Slater's rules"). The value of σ appropriate to any electron under consideration is made up as follows:

1. No contribution from any principal quantum shell outside the one considered.

2. 0.35 from each other electron in the same group. (For this purpose, the groups are 1*s*; 2*s* and 2*p*; 3*s* and 3*p*; 3*d*; 4*s* and 4*p*; 4*d*; 4*f*; etc.) However, 0.30 is used for 1*s*.

3. If the group considered is *s* and *p*, 0.85 from each electron with $n - 1$ and 1.00 from each electron farther in; if the group considered is *d* or *f*, 1.00 from each electron of a preceding group.

As an example, the shielding constants for vanadium

$$(1s^2 2s^2 2p^6 3s^2 3p^6 3d^3 4s^2)$$

are obtained as shown in Table 1-2. It might be noted that such an application of Slater's rules shows that for the vanadium atom the 3*d*

Table 1-2 *Slater parameters for vanadium*

1*s*	$\sigma = 0.30$	$Z - \sigma = 22.70$
2*s* and 2*p*	$\sigma = 2(0.85) + 7(0.35)$	$Z - \sigma = 18.85$
3*s* and 3*p*	$\sigma = 2(1.00) + 8(0.85) + 7(0.35)$	$Z - \sigma = 12.75$
3*d*	$\sigma = 2(1.00) + 8(1.00) + 8(1.00) + 2(0.35)$	$Z - \sigma = 4.30$
4*s*	$\sigma = 2(1.00) + 8(1.00) + 11(0.85) + 1(0.35)$	$Z - \sigma = 3.30$

electrons are more tightly bound (higher effective nuclear charge) than the $4s$. Hence, in ionization of a neutral vanadium atom, the electron removed first is a $4s$. On the other hand, a similar calculation for potassium ($Z = 19$) shows that the $4s$ electron is bound more tightly than the $3d$.

It should be emphasized that Slater's rules were formulated empirically to account for observed energy-dependent properties such as ionization potentials, electric and magnetic susceptibilities, X-ray scattering factors, etc. Although the rules work reasonably well for the first few periods, they become less reliable when the principal quantum number is greater than four.

When a many-electron atom consists of closed electronic shells and one additional electron, or when it is one electron short of a closed configuration, it is possible to describe the electron probability distribution by using Slater radial functions and one-electron angular wave functions of the type given in Section 1-1. For more complex cases, electron-electron interactions need to be taken into account.

• 1-3 Vector Model of the Atom

The quantum numbers n, l, and m which appear in the solutions of the Schrödinger equation can be visualized in terms of the following simplified model. The principal quantum number n denotes qualitatively the distance from the nucleus to the maximum in the radial distribution. The orbital quantum number l characterizes the angular momentum—i.e., the angular velocity times the moment of inertia. For an s electron ($l = 0$) the angular momentum is zero. For p, d, f electrons ($l = 1, 2, 3$, respectively), the angular momentum progressively increases as given by the formula

$$\text{angular momentum} = \sqrt{l(l+1)}\,\frac{h}{2\pi}$$

The magnetic quantum number m (sometimes also written m_l) gives the projection of the angular momentum vector with respect to an external field direction. For an electron of given l value, the maximum observable component of angular momentum in the field direction is $+l(h/2\pi)$. If the momentum is oriented opposite to the field direction, the component is a minimum and is equal to $-l(h/2\pi)$. The only permitted intermediate values are $m(h/2\pi)$, where m is quantized and can take on only integral values between $+l$ and $-l$. For example, for a d electron ($l = 2$), the observed angular momentum component can only be

$$\frac{h}{\pi} \qquad \frac{h}{2\pi} \qquad 0 \qquad -\frac{h}{2\pi} \qquad -\frac{h}{\pi}$$

It might be noted that the observed angular momentum component never quite equals the angular momentum, which is

$$\sqrt{l(l+1)}\,\frac{h}{2\pi} = \sqrt{6}\,\frac{h}{2\pi} \qquad \text{for } l = 2$$

This limitation is a consequence of the uncertainty principle, which does not allow precise alignment of the angular momentum vector with the field direction. Precise alignment would require that the other two components of the vector be zero, thereby defining all three components. Such total specification violates the uncertainty principle.

There is a fourth quantum number which does not come out of the Schrödinger wave equation and which is the one used to describe the electron spin. The spin angular momentum of an electron can have two orientations (parallel or antiparallel) with respect to an external field direction. The spin quantum number m_s can have values $+\frac{1}{2}$ or $-\frac{1}{2}$ corresponding to spin momentum of $\frac{1}{2}(h/2\pi)$ or $-\frac{1}{2}(h/2\pi)$.

According to the Pauli exclusion principle, no two electrons in the same atom can be identical in all four quantum numbers.

In a many-electron atom, the electrons do not behave independently in an external field but are coupled together. Thus, there is for any atom a resultant angular momentum characterized by the quantum number J which arises from the combined effect of the spin and orbital angular momenta of all electrons in the atom. In atoms of relatively low atomic number, the coupling is of the type called Russell-Saunders, or LS, coupling. For this interaction, the individual spins couple as a unit to give a resultant spin, S, and the individual orbital angular momenta couple as a unit to give a resultant orbital moment, L.

For a given value of L and of S, J can take on quantized values ranging from $L - S$ to $L + S$. Since S can be integral or half-integral, J values for a fixed L and S must be either all integral or all half-integral.

The following examples illustrate the use of the quantum numbers J, L, and S. Let us consider first the case of the lithium atom in its ground (or lowest-energy) state. With $Z = 3$, lithium has three electrons, two of which have paired spins in the inner shell, leaving one unpaired electron in the outer shell. The inner shell, being complete, does not contribute to L (because for this case $m_l = 0$ for both of the $1s$ electrons) nor to S (because $m_s = +\frac{1}{2}$ for one electron cancels $m_s = -\frac{1}{2}$ for the other). L, S, and hence J are determined by the outer electron. For the $2s$ electron $m_l = 0$, so the total L for the atom is zero. However, the electron is unpaired, so $m_s = +\frac{1}{2}$ or $-\frac{1}{2}$ is uncompensated and $S = \frac{1}{2}$. By convention, only the positive sign is chosen because in the absence of any external field there is only one state. Thus there is only the J value $+\frac{1}{2}$.

In the presence of an external magnetic field there will be two states, one with the J vector oriented parallel to the field and the other with the J vector opposed to the field. Because there is the possibility of these two states, the ground state is referred to as a doublet. The ground state, sometimes called the ground term, is symbolized by ${}^2S_{1/2}$, which is called the term symbol. The superscript denotes the multiplicity—i.e., the number of possible orientations of S—and is equal to $2S + 1$. The letter reflects the value of L and is S for $L = 0$, P for $L = 1$, D for $L = 2$, F for $L = 3$, G for $L = 4$, H for $L = 5$, and I for $L = 6$. The subscript gives the value of J.

The ground state of aluminum ($Z = 13$) is ${}^2P_{1/2}$, which arises from the following electron configuration:

	$1s$	$2s$	$2p$			$3s$	$3p$		
	⇅	⇅	⇅	⇅	⇅	⇅	↑	—	—
$m_l =$	0	0	+1	0	−1	0	+1	0	−1

The horizontal dashes represent orbitals, the arrows give the spin population, and the values of m_l refer to the relative spatial orientation of each electron. Complete subshells again contribute nothing to L or S. For the $2p$ subshell, the total contribution from the two electrons with $m_l = +1$ is compensated by the contribution from the two with $m_l = -1$. The only net contribution to L comes from the one electron in a $3p$ orbital. In the absence of an external electric field, all three of the $3p$ orbitals are degenerate (of equal energy), so that it matters not which of the orbitals is occupied. By convention, the term symbol is figured by using the orbital of maximum m_l, since this is the one favored if an external field is applied. Thus, $L = 1$, and we are concerned with a P state. With only one unpaired electron, $S = \frac{1}{2}$ and the state is a spin doublet. For J there are two possible values, $L + S = 1 + \frac{1}{2} = \frac{3}{2}$ and $L - S = \frac{1}{2}$.

On the basis of complete spectral analysis, particularly the splitting of spectral lines in a magnetic field (Zeeman effect), there have been formulated a series of empirical rules called Hund's rules, from which the lowest state can be predicted. For a given subshell population, Hund's rules state:

1. The state of maximum S has lowest energy.
2. For the same S, the state of maximum L is lowest.
3. For given L and S, the state of minimum $J(= L - S)$ is favored when the subshell is less than half-filled and that of maximum $J(= L + S)$, when more than half-filled.

On the basis of Hund's rules, the ground terms for the next few elements following aluminum are given in Table 1-3.

Table 1-3 *Ground terms*

Si	$Z = 14$	$1s^22s^22p^63s^23p^2$	$^3P_0$
P	$Z = 15$	$1s^22s^22p^63s^23p^3$	$^4S_{3/2}$
S	$Z = 16$	$1s^22s^22p^63s^23p^4$	$^3P_2$
Cl	$Z = 17$	$1s^22s^22p^63s^23p^5$	$^2P_{3/2}$
Ar	$Z = 18$	$1s^22s^22p^63s^23p^6$	$^1S_0$

Term symbols are also used to describe states of ions. For example, the ground term of the tripositive holmium ion ($Z = 67$) is $^5I_8$. The electronic configuration is

$$1s^22s^22p^63s^23p^63d^{10}4s^24p^64d^{10}5s^25p^6$$

and $$4f\text{:}\ \underline{\uparrow\downarrow}\ \underline{\uparrow\downarrow}\ \underline{\uparrow\downarrow}\ \underline{\uparrow}\ \underline{\uparrow}\ \underline{\uparrow}\ \underline{\uparrow}$$

$$m_l = +3\ \ +2\ \ +1\ \ 0\ \ -1\ \ -2\ \ -3$$

It can be seen that $S = 2$ and $L = 6$. Since the subshell is more than half-filled, Hund's third rule predicts that the lowest state will be the one with maximum J(S and L parallel). Thus the completed term symbol is $^5I_8$.

It must be emphasized that the assumption of Russell-Saunders coupling is not applicable in all cases. Particularly for atoms of high atomic number and for atoms that are highly ionized, the spin of an individual electron couples directly with the angular orbital moment of that same electron to give an individual j for that electron. The j then couples with other j's to form a resultant J for the whole atom. This type of coupling is known as j-j coupling and is quite important for the actinide elements.

• 1-4 Magnetic Properties of Atoms

In favorable cases, a confirmation of the assignment of term symbol and hence electronic configuration can be obtained from magnetic measurements. The magnetization of any substance is in general proportional to the magnetic field in which the substance is placed. The proportionality constant (magnetization per unit field) is called the magnetic susceptibility of the sample. When expressed per unit volume, the susceptibility is usually represented by κ, the volume magnetic susceptibility; per gram, by χ, the gram or mass magnetic susceptibility; per mole, by χ_M, the molar magnetic susceptibility.

If the susceptibility is high, is a function of the magnetic field strength, and shows hysteresis, the substance is said to be ferromagnetic. Ferromagnetism requires a coupling of the magnetic moments of large numbers of atoms and is not a property of isolated atoms. Its consideration will be postponed to Section 3-6.

If the susceptibility is not dependent on the field and is positive in sign—i.e., the magnetization is in the same direction as the externally applied field—the substance is said to be paramagnetic. Diamagnetic substances, on the other hand, are those with negative susceptibilities, still, however, independent of the field strength. Paramagnetism and diamagnetism are atomic properties.

Diamagnetism arises from the fact that electrical charges—e.g., electrons—move in such a way as to counteract the effect of an externally applied magnetic field. For the Avogadro number, N, of atoms the molar diamagnetic susceptibility is given by

$$\chi_M = -\frac{e^2 N}{6m} \sum_{i=1}^{Z} \overline{r_i^2}$$

where e is the electronic charge, m is the electron mass, and $\overline{r_i^2}$ is the average square distance of electron i from the nucleus. The summation extends over all the electrons in the atom, with the biggest contribution coming from the outer parts of the electron distribution. (In principle, any collection of electrical charges has a diamagnetic susceptibility, but because of the inverse dependence on mass, it is negligible for all except the lightest of particles. Also, it is always negative regardless of the charge on the particles.)

Although it is possible to calculate diamagnetic susceptibilities once the electron wave functions are known, in practice values for atomic diamagnetism are assigned on the basis of experimental measurements on various substances containing the atom in question. Representative values for the alkali cations are: Li^+, -0.7×10^{-6}; Na^+, -6.1×10^{-6}; K^+, -14.6×10^{-6}; Rb^+, -22.0×10^{-6}; Cs^+, -35.1×10^{-6}. These values are in units of ergs per square gauss per mole, and are temperature-independent.

In addition to diamagnetism, which is present in all atoms, there is for many atoms a positive residue after subtraction of the diamagnetism from the measured susceptibility. This positive contribution is called the paramagnetism.

$$\chi = \chi_{\text{dia}} + \chi_{\text{para}}$$

Besides the sign difference between χ_{dia} and χ_{para}, the paramagnetic susceptibility is generally larger in magnitude and decreases with rising temperature. Temperature-dependent paramagnetism arises from the existence of permanent magnetic moments in the atoms, which come from uncompensated electron spin and in some cases from uncompensated orbital motion of the electrons.

The temperature dependence of paramagnetism is given by the Curie-Weiss law,

$$\chi_{\text{para}} = \chi - \chi_{\text{dia}} = \frac{C}{T - \Delta}$$

where C is a constant related to the permanent atomic moment and Δ is a Curie temperature, sometimes called the Weiss constant. Below the Curie temperature, which is characteristic of each substance, the Curie-Weiss law no longer holds, because the atomic moments lock together in a cooperative assembly so that the material exhibits behavior of a ferromagnetic type. The magnitude of Δ gives a measure of the strength of the cooperative interactions. For ideal paramagnetic substances, Δ would be zero. For ferromagnetic materials such as iron, cobalt, nickel, Fe_3O_4, etc., cooperative interactions leading to parallel alignment of atomic moments are so strong that Curie temperatures are above room temperature. In other cases—e.g., Gd, EuO, EuS—cooperative interactions are weaker and lead to Curie temperatures considerably below room temperature. For substances such as CoO there are strong interactions which favor antiparallel alignment of atomic moments, so that below a characteristic temperature (Néel temperature) the magnetic susceptibility decreases with decreasing temperature. In the ideal case or for any real substance at sufficiently high temperature, the interactions between atomic magnetic moments are negligible and the paramagnetic susceptibility follows the Curie law,

$$\chi = \frac{C}{T}$$

To relate the measured paramagnetism to atomic moments we can consider the problem of N independent atomic magnetic moments μ in a field of strength H. The paramagnetic susceptibility χ is given by

$$\chi = \frac{N\bar{\mu}}{H}$$

where $\bar{\mu}$ differs from μ in being the average effective moment contributed by each atom, allowing for the fact that thermal motion prevents perfect alignment of μ with H. An expression for $\bar{\mu}$ can be obtained by summing over all orientations, taking into account the contribution of each orientation and its relative population. The relative population can be found by noting that the different orientations in the field correspond to different energies and that the distribution over these various energy states is governed by the Boltzmann distribution law. The contribution to $\bar{\mu}$ by the fraction of atoms having a particular value of θ (angle between μ and H) is given by

$$\mu_\theta = (\mu \cos \theta) \exp\left(\frac{\mu H \cos \theta}{kT}\right)$$

where $\mu \cos \theta$ represents the component of μ along H and the exponential term is the Boltzmann factor. For $\mu H \cos \theta \ll kT$, the exponential can be expanded and approximated by $1 + (\mu H \cos\theta)/kT$, where higher-order terms have been neglected. (The approximation breaks down at high fields and at low temperatures.)

Thus, μ, which is the average of μ_θ over all values of θ, is given by

$$\bar{\mu} = \overline{\mu \cos\theta\left(1 + \frac{\mu H \cos\theta}{kT}\right)}$$

$$= \overline{\mu \cos\theta} + \frac{\overline{\mu^2 H \cos^2\theta}}{kT}$$

$$= 0 + \frac{1}{3}\frac{\mu^2 H}{kT}$$

It should be recalled that the average, designated by superlines, is zero for $\cos\theta$ and $\frac{1}{3}$ for $\cos^2\theta$. For a collection of N atoms, the magnetic susceptibility is

$$\chi = \frac{N\mu^2}{3kT}$$

The Curie constant C is thus seen to be $(N\mu^2)/3k$, where N is the Avogadro number. Since C is an experimentally determined quantity, μ can be found from the experimental data. In Bohr magneton units μ is $2.83\sqrt{C}$.

The next question concerns the relation between μ and the electron configuration. Because both the electron spin and the orbital motion may contribute to μ, the relation is not a simple one. In fact, it is made more complicated by the fact that the spin moment is twice as effective as the orbital moment. This unequal weighting is described by the so-called g factor, or Lande splitting factor, which for isolated atoms has the form

$$g = 1 + \frac{J(J+1) + S(S+1) - L(L+1)}{2J(J+1)}$$

Defining g in this way, the magnetic moment μ is given, in units of Bohr magnetons, by

$$\mu = g\sqrt{J(J+1)}$$

It should be noted that μ is not equal to gJ, as might be expected for a vector J units long. The problem is the same as that previously noted with respect to the maximum observable component of angular momentum (page 17).

The lanthanide ions, corresponding as they do to incomplete inner shells shielded from the influence of neighboring atoms, provide a test for comparison of observed and calculated magnetic moments. Table 1-4 lists electronic configurations, ground-term symbols, g values,

Table 1-4 *Paramagnetic moments of lanthanide ions*

Ion	$4f^n$	term	g	μ(calc.)	μ(expt.)
La^{+3}	0	$^1S_0$	1	0	0
Ce^{+3}	1	$^2F_{5/2}$	$\frac{6}{7}$	2.54	2.5
Pr^{+3}	2	$^3H_4$	$\frac{4}{5}$	3.58	3.5
Nd^{+3}	3	$^4I_{9/2}$	$\frac{8}{11}$	3.62	3.6
Pm^{+3}	4	$^5I_4$	$\frac{3}{5}$	2.68	
Sm^{+3}	5	$^6H_{5/2}$	$\frac{2}{7}$	0.84	1.5
Eu^{+3}	6	$^7F_0$	1	0	3.4
Gd^{+3}	7	$^8S_{7/2}$	2	7.94	8.0
Tb^{+3}	8	$^7F_6$	$\frac{3}{2}$	9.72	9.3
Dy^{+3}	9	$^6H_{15/2}$	$\frac{4}{3}$	10.63	10.6
Ho^{+3}	10	$^5I_8$	$\frac{5}{4}$	10.60	10.4
Er^{+3}	11	$^4I_{15/2}$	$\frac{6}{5}$	9.59	9.5
Tm^{+3}	12	$^3H_6$	$\frac{7}{6}$	7.57	7.4
Yb^{+3}	13	$^2F_{7/2}$	$\frac{8}{7}$	4.54	4.5
Lu^{+3}	14	$^1S_0$	1	0	0

and calculated and observed moments. As can be seen, the agreement between calculated and experimental moments is reasonably good except for Sm^{+3} and Eu^{+3}. In both of these cases, there are low-lying excited states which are appreciably populated at room temperature and which have moments higher than those of the ground states.

Ions owing their paramagnetism to d electrons instead of f electrons do not show the same satisfactory agreement between observed magnetic moments and those calculated for gaseous ions with Russell-Saunders coupling. The reason is that unpaired d electrons, unlike the f electrons in the lanthanides, are imperfectly shielded from interaction with local fields. The effect of the local fields, arising from neighboring atoms, is in first approximation to destroy, or "quench," the orbital contribution to the total magnetic moment. The "quenching" can be visualized as arising from the nonspherical symmetry of the orbital electron distribution (for incomplete subshells). Electrical interactions with surrounding atoms effectively "lock" the orbitals into preferred positions, thus preventing orientation of the orbital magnetic moment by an externally applied magnetic field. Described more rigorously, the environmental electric fields can be said to destroy L as a meaningful quantum number. The observed magnetic moment corresponds closely to that of electron spin only. The "spin-only" moment can be calculated from the number of unpaired electrons in the ion. More specifically, if L is quenched, $J = S$ and

$$g = 1 + \frac{J(J+1) + S(S+1) - L(L+1)}{2J(J+1)}$$

$$= 1 + \frac{S(S+1) + S(S+1)}{2S(S+1)} = 2$$

From the previously given equation

$$\mu = g\sqrt{J(J+1)}$$

the magnetic moment turns out to be

$$\mu = 2\sqrt{S(S+1)}$$

For an ion containing n unpaired electrons, each of spin $\frac{1}{2}$, the total spin S is $n/2$, so that the magnetic moment in Bohr magnetons is

$$\mu = 2\sqrt{\frac{n}{2}\left(\frac{n}{2}+1\right)} = \sqrt{n(n+2)}$$

Table 1-5 compares some observed magnetic moments, for hydrated ions, with those calculated using the spin-only formula. It should be noted that when the *d* subshell is more than half filled the experimental moments are invariably greater than those calculated by

Table 1-5 *Paramagnetic moments of some transition ions*

Ion	Configuration	n	μ(calc.)	μ(expt.)
Sc^{+3}	d^0	0	0	0
Ti^{+3}	d^1	1	1.73	1.75
Ti^{++}	d^2	2	2.84	2.76
V^{++}	d^3	3	3.87	3.86
Cr^{++}	d^4	4	4.90	4.80
Mn^{++}	d^5	5	5.92	5.96
Fe^{++}	d^6	4	4.90	5.0–5.5
Co^{++}	d^7	3	3.87	4.4–5.2
Ni^{++}	d^8	2	2.84	2.9–3.4
Cu^{++}	d^9	1	1.73	1.8–2.2
Zn^{++}	d^{10}	0	0	0

"spin-only." For these cases the orbital moment is said to be incompletely quenched.

For certain compounds—e.g., $K_4Fe(CN)_6$, which is diamagnetic—interaction of the transition metal atom with its coordinating neighbors (ligands) may be so great that the number of unpaired electrons is changed from that predicted by Hund's rules. We shall consider this problem in Chapter 2.

• 1-5 Electronic Spectra

In inorganic chemistry the electronic spectra of isolated atoms or ions are not usually dealt with. However, the spectra of solutions or solids, which are usually the ones encountered, have certain features in common with those of gaseous ions. Thus we can now discuss the general characteristics of spectra and defer until later detailed consideration of the influence neighboring atoms may have in modifying atomic spectra.

It will be recalled that absorption spectra consist of lines or bands which appear as minima in a plot of transmission vs. frequency. Alternatively, spectra are sometimes presented as plots of absorbency (logarithm of ratio of incident light to transmitted light) vs. frequency (or, often, wavelength). The informative features of absorption bands are: frequency or wavelength of the maximum absorption, intensity of the absorption as measured by either maximum absorbency value or by area of the band, and sharpness or width of the band at half-maximum height. A line in an absorption spectrum (or one in an emission spectrum) has a frequency ν which is proportional to the energy of the quantum absorbed (or emitted). The energy of the quantum absorbed is $h\nu$ (where h is the Planck constant) and is equal to the difference in energy between the final and initial states of the atom,

$$h\nu = E_2 - E_1$$

In the visible range, corresponding to wavelengths between 7000 and 4000 A, frequencies lie between 4.3×10^{14} and 7.5×10^{14} cycles per sec. These are equivalent to energy differences of 41 and 72 kcal per mole. Transitions between electronic states of atoms can have any energy ranging up to the ionization energies. For cesium, which has the lowest ionization energy of any neutral atom, ionization occurs at 90 kcal per mole. Thus electronic transitions can occur with frequencies anywhere in the electromagnetic spectrum—e.g., radiofrequency, the infrared, the visible, or the ultraviolet.

The probability that a given spectral transition occurs depends upon the extent to which the wave functions of the initial and final states combine to give a net electric moment. If there is no net moment—e.g., for symmetry reasons—transition between the two states is said to be "forbidden." Some "forbidden" transitions do occur but with intensities that are orders of magnitude lower than for "allowed" transitions. Rules for deciding whether particular transitions are "forbidden" or "allowed" are called *selection rules*. A simple summary in terms of the atomic quantum numbers L, S, and J is as follows:

1. L changes by ± 1
2. Transitions in which S changes are not allowed
3. J changes by ± 1 or 0 but the transition $J = 0$ to $J = 0$ is not allowed.

In general, spectra of isolated atoms consist of sharp lines whose observed width is usually limited by the slit width of the spectrometer used in the experiment. However, the lines are not infinitely sharp. They possess intrinsic width due to the uncertainty principle and to

Doppler and pressure broadening. The uncertainty principle implies that the shorter-lived an energy state is, the less precisely its energy is defined. Doppler broadening is due to motion of the atoms with respect to the observer; pressure broadening is caused by perturbations of electronic states by collision with other atoms. In condensed phases, spectral features are considerably more complex and lines are characteristically broader because of interaction with the environment.

• 1-6 Ionization Potential

The ionization potential is defined as the energy required to remove an electron from a gaseous species. First, second, third, etc., potentials for elements refer to successive removal of electrons from an originally neutral atom. It might also be noted that there are ionization potentials which can be used to describe electron removal from molecules.

The usual method for determining ionization potentials is from spectral limits—that is, from the frequency limit where the spectrum changes from discrete lines to a continuum. At the frequency limit corresponding to the ionization potential, an electron is captured or ejected with zero kinetic energy. Frequencies higher than this limit correspond to capture or ejection of an electron with finite kinetic energy. Since kinetic energy is effectively unquantized, a continuous range is possible.

Values for successive ionization potentials are listed in Table 1-6. They are given in electron volts, where 1 ev is 1.60×10^{-12} erg, corresponding to 23.066 kcal per mole. The specific values observed depend on the atomic size and on the nuclear charge screened by intervening electrons (cf. Slater's rules, Section 1-2). For larger atoms of comparable effective nuclear charge, the ionization requires less energy. Also, the higher the charge on the species from which the electron is being removed, the higher the ionization potential. Finally, there is a strong dependence on the electron configuration, and the enhanced stability of filled and half-filled shells is clearly evident.

In chemical reactions, it is always necessary to shift electrons and thereby work against the binding energy. Therefore, the ionization potential is a starting point in evaluating the energy balance. However, only rarely is removal complete and energy equal to the ionization potential involved. For complete analysis, consideration must be given to what happens to the electron—i.e., the energy liberated on its capture by another atom—and to the electrical readjust-

Table 1-6 *Ionization potentials (in ev)*

Atomic number	Symbol	I	II	III	IV	V	VI	VII	VIII
1	H	13.60							
2	He	24.58	54.40						
3	Li	5.39	75.62	122.42					
4	Be	9.32	18.21	153.85	217.66				
5	B	8.30	25.15	37.92	259.30	340.13			
6	C	11.26	24.38	47.86	64.48	391.99	489.84		
7	N	14.54	29.61	47.43	77.45	97.86	551.93	666.83	
8	O	13.61	35.15	54.93	77.39	113.87	138.08	739.11	871.12
9	F	17.42	34.98	62.65	87.23	114.21	157.12	185.14	953.60
10	Ne	21.56	41.07	64	97.16	126.4	157.91		
11	Na	5.14	47.29	71.65	98.88	138.60	172.36	208.44	264.16
12	Mg	7.64	15.03	80.12	109.29	141.23	186.86	225.31	265.97
13	Al	5.98	18.82	28.44	119.96	153.77	190.42	241.93	285.13
14	Si	8.15	16.34	33.46	45.13	166.73	205.11	246.41	303.87
15	P	11.0	19.65	30.16	51.35	65.01	220.41	263.31	309.26
16	S	10.36	23.4	35.0	47.29	72.5	88.03	280.99	328.80
17	Cl	13.01	23.80	39.90	53.5	67.80	96.7	114.27	348.3
18	Ar	15.76	27.62	40.90	59.79	75.0	91.3	124.0	143.46
19	K	4.34	31.81	46	60.90		99.7	118	155
20	Ca	6.11	11.87	51.21	67	84.39		128	147
21	Sc	6.56	12.89	24.75	73.9	92	111.1		159
22	Ti	6.83	13.63	28.14	43.24	99.8	120	140.8	
23	V	6.74	14.2	29.7	48	65.2	128.9	151	173.7
24	Cr	6.76	16.6	31?	50.4?	72.8?			
25	Mn	7.43	15.70	32?	52?	75.7?			
26	Fe	7.90	16.16						
27	Co	7.86	17.3						
28	Ni	7.63	18.2						
29	Cu	7.72	20.34	29.5					
30	Zn	9.39	17.89	40.0					
31	Ga	6.00	20.43	30.6	63.8				
32	Ge	8.13	15.86	34.07	45.5	93.0			
33	As	10?	20.1	28.0	49.9	62.5			
34	Se	9.75	21.3	33.9	42.72	72.8	81.4		
35	Br	11.84	19.1	25.7	50?				
36	Kr	14.00	26.4	36.8	68?				
37	Rb	4.18	27.36	47?	80?				
38	Sr	5.69	10.98						
39	Y	6.6	12.3	20.4					
40	Zr	6.95	13.97	24.00	33.8				
41	Nb	6.77		24.2					
42	Mo	7.18							
43	Tc								
44	Ru	7.5							
45	Rh	7.7							
46	Pd	8.33	19.8						
47	Ag	7.57	21.4	35.9					
48	Cd	8.99	16.84	38.0					
49	In	5.79	18.79	27.9	57.8				
50	Sn	7.33	14.5	30.5	39.4	80.7			
51	Sb	8.64	18?	24.7	44.0	55.5			
52	Te	9.01		30.5	37.7	60.0	72?		
53	I	10.44	19.4						

Table 1-6 (continued)

Atomic number	Symbol	I	II	III	IV	V	VI	VII	VIII
54	Xe	12.13	21.1?	32.0	46?	76?			
55	Cs	3.89	23.4	35?	51?	58?			
56	Ba	5.21	9.95						
57	La	5.61	11.4	20.4?					
58	Ce	6.9?	14.8						
59	Pr	5.8?							
60	Nd	6.3?							
61	Pm								
62	Sm	5.6	11.4						
63	Eu	5.67	11.4						
64	Gd	6.16							
65	Tb	6.7?							
66	Dy	6.8?							
67	Ho								
68	Er								
69	Tm								
70	Yb	6.2							
71	Lu	5.0							
72	Hf	5.5?	14.8?						
73	Ta	6?							
74	W	7.98							
75	Re	7.87							
76	Os	8.7							
77	Ir	9.2							
78	Pt	8.96							
79	Au	9.22	19.95						
80	Hg	10.43	18.65	34.3	72?	82?			
81	Tl	6.11	20.32	29.7	50.5				
82	Pb	7.42	14.96	31.9?	42.11	69.4			
83	Bi	8?	16.6	25.42	45.1	55.7			
84	Po								
85	At								
86	Rn	10.75							
87	Fr								
88	Ra	5.28	10.10						
89	Ac								
90	Th			29.4					
91	Pa								
92	U	4?							

ment both of the two-atom system and of all surrounding atoms. Most chemical species end up in condensed phases, where the dielectric rearrangement of the entire medium often plays a decisive role.

• 1-7 Electron Affinity

The electron affinity is defined as the energy liberated when a gaseous species captures an electron (of zero kinetic energy). Evidently, electron affinity is equal in magnitude to the ionization energy for the species formed. Thus Table 1-6 also gives electron affinities for positive ions of the elements. The formation of negative ions by the addition of electrons to neutral atoms is not generally studied by conventional spectroscopy. Instead, values of electron affinity are obtained either by analysis of energy cycles in which one step is electron capture or by the direct study of electron capture from heated filaments. In the latter method the numbers of neutral atoms, negative ions, and electrons are determined—e.g., with mass spectrometry. This gives directly the standard free energy for the equilibrium

$$X + e^- \rightleftharpoons X^-$$

The energy can be calculated from the temperature dependence of the equilibrium constant.

Recent values of electron affinity found for those few elements which have been measured are given in Table 1-7. It might be noted

Table 1-7 *Electron affinities (in kcal/mole)*

Process	Energy released
$F + e^- \rightarrow F^-$	83
$Cl + e^- \rightarrow Cl^-$	86.5
$Br + e^- \rightarrow Br^-$	81.5
$I + e^- \rightarrow I^-$	74.2
$H + e \rightarrow H^-$	16.5
$O + e^- \rightarrow O^-$	About 30
$O + 2e^- \rightarrow O^=$	About −170
$S + e^- \rightarrow S^-$	About 40
$S + 2e^- \rightarrow S^=$	About −90

that the values for the halogens do not show a monotonic decrease, as might be expected for going down a group of the periodic table. The unexpected increase from fluorine to chlorine also shows up in going from oxygen to sulfur. The reason for the negative values for the formation of $O^=$ and $S^=$ is that the second electron must be added to an already negative ion. Because the values are negative, energy must be supplied by another process in order to form either $O^=$ or $S^=$.

• Supplementary Reading

In addition to other monographs of this series, the following references should prove helpful:

1. Gerhard Herzberg, "Atomic Spectra and Atomic Structure," Dover, New York, 1944.
2. Linus Pauling and E. Bright Wilson, "Introduction to Quantum Mechanics," McGraw-Hill, New York, 1935.
3. H. Eyring, J. Walter, and G. E. Kimball, "Quantum Chemistry," Wiley, New York, 1944.
4. W. Kauzman, "Quantum Chemistry," Academic Press, New York, 1957.
5. O. K. Rice, "Electronic Structure and Chemical Binding," McGraw-Hill, New York, 1940.

2

Molecules

At its most fundamental level chemistry is the binding of atoms to each other. Although any aggregate so formed may be called a "molecule," the term is usually reserved for neutral species consisting of relatively few atoms held together sufficiently strongly to retain identity through a variety of conditions.

• 2-1 Description of Molecules

Practically all of the interaction between atoms in molecules is electrical in origin. However, only in a few special cases can the interaction be considered as a simple attraction between oppositely charged ions. In the general case, the electrical interaction involved is between the fundamental particles—e.g., electrons and protons—that make up the molecule. Thus, in principle, it should be possible to construct from known physical principles a molecular charge distribution which would enable calculation of the various structural and energetic features of the molecule.

Just as it is impossible to treat precisely a many-electron atom, so it is impossible to treat precisely molecules containing several electrons and several nuclei. Obviously, it is necessary to make simplifying approximations and, equally obviously, there may be several alternate postulates which can be introduced. The usual approximations in some way involve reference to isolated atoms and assume that only limited changes can occur in the process of molecule formation. In the valence-bond approach, the first of the methods we shall consider, it is assumed that the atoms retain complete identity and the only change that occurs on molecule formation is an exchange of electrons between orbitals of adjacent atoms. In the molecular-orbital method as usually employed—that is, linear combination of atomic orbitals (LCAO)—it is assumed that the electrons in molecules occupy orbitals which arise directly from combination of the atomic orbitals involved. In ligand field theory, orbitals of a central atom orient themselves spatially so as to give the most favorable interaction energy between the central atom and surrounding ligands.

• 2-2 Valence Bond

A reasonably simple molecule that illustrates the details of valence-bond theory is the ammonia molecule. Suppose we start with the information that the ammonia molecule consists of a nitrogen atom to which are bound three hydrogen atoms. The assumption might then be made that the nitrogen atom is identical with any isolated N atom—specifically, that it has the electron configuration $1s^2 2s^2 2p^3$, or $1s^2 2s^2 2p_x^1 2p_y^1 2p_z^1$. Likewise, the hydrogen atoms are assumed to have their usual configuration, $1s^1$.

The essence of valence-bond theory is that an unpaired electron in an orbital of one atom—e.g., p_x of the N atom—undergoes exchange interaction with an unpaired electron in an orbital of an adjacent atom—e.g., $1s$ of H atom. The exchange, which comes about because of the indistinguishability of electrons, implies that the electron on the N atom can exchange places with the electron on the H atom. The exchange can be expressed by taking combinations of the wave functions appropriate to the system before and after exchange such as

$$\psi_{p_x}^{\mathrm{N}}(1)\psi_s^{\mathrm{H}}(2) \pm \psi_{p_x}^{\mathrm{N}}(2)\psi_s^{\mathrm{H}}(1)$$

where 1 and 2 designate the electrons and $\psi_{p_x}^{\mathrm{N}}$ and ψ_s^{H} designate orbitals of the N and H atoms, respectively. The individual wave functions are referred to coordinate systems centered at the respective nuclei.

Thus $\psi_{p_x}^{N}(1)\psi_s^{H}(2)$ is a combined wave function describing the situation where electron 1 has wave function $\psi_{p_x}^{N}$ while simultaneously electron 2 has wave function ψ_s^{H}. The second term $\psi_{p_x}^{N}(2)\psi_s^{H}(1)$ is simply the reverse. Because of the Pauli exclusion principle, the wave function above that has the plus sign between the first and second terms is permitted only when the two electrons differ in spin.

Another way of saying this is that the two electrons can be exchanged—that is, effectively occupy the same regions in space—only if their spins are opposed. The wave function above that has the minus sign between the first and second terms is permitted only if the two electrons have parallel spin. In this case, however, the distribution has a lower probability between the nuclei and corresponds to a repulsive state. Because the electron distribution of the spin-paired (antiparallel) state is characterized by an enhancement of negative charge in the region between the nuclei, the state is an attractive state and is of lower energy than the repulsive state. Thus two electrons of opposite spin are regarded in valence-bond theory as being responsible for the binding of two adjacent atoms and this corresponds to the shared pair bond.

The model just described for the ammonia molecule would lead to three valence bonds at right angles to each other corresponding to use of p_x, p_y, and p_z orbitals. However, the NH_3 molecule in fact has H—N—H bond angles of 107.3°. Although proton-proton repulsion would be expected to open the bond angle from 90°, it seems that this effect is not sufficient to give the observed angle. A more refined valence-bond approach, which gives a closer approximation to the experimental observation, is based on the concept of orbital hybridization.

• 2-3 Hybrid Orbitals

The concept of independent electron orbitals is an oversimplification even in the case of a many-electron *atom* and it becomes less tenable for the more complex case of molecules. To counteract this weakness and thus improve the description of molecular structures and energies, the hybrid-orbital approximation has been introduced. The essence of this method is the replacement of a set of hydrogen-like atomic orbitals by new wave functions that contain the combined characteristics of the hydrogen functions.

As a specific example we consider hybridization of an *s* orbital and a *p* orbital to form two *sp* hybrids. (It is a general rule that the number of independent combined wave functions is equal to the number of orbitals available for the combination.) The process of hybridization can be represented mathematically as an addition of individual wave functions with appropriate normalizing factors as coefficients. In the case of the *sp* hybrid the two resultant wave functions are

$$\psi_1 = \frac{1}{\sqrt{2}}\psi_s + \frac{1}{\sqrt{2}}\psi_p$$

$$\psi_2 = \frac{1}{\sqrt{2}}\psi_s - \frac{1}{\sqrt{2}}\psi_p$$

the angular dependences of which are given by

$$\psi_{sp} = \frac{1}{\sqrt{2}}(\psi_s \pm \psi_p) = \frac{1}{\sqrt{8\pi}}(1 \pm \sqrt{3}\cos\theta)$$

and are represented in Figure 2-1. ψ_1 and ψ_2 are centered on the same origin and differ only in that one results in high electron probability on one side of the nucleus and the other on the other side. Use of these two equivalent hybrid orbitals for binding two additional atoms leads to a linear molecule. Such a description, for example, will account for the observed linear shape of $HgCl_2$, where the two valence electrons of the Hg are assigned to the two hybrid orbitals constructed from the 6*s* and a 6*p* orbital. The actual hybridization is by itself an energy-requiring process; it occurs only because the resultant bonds are

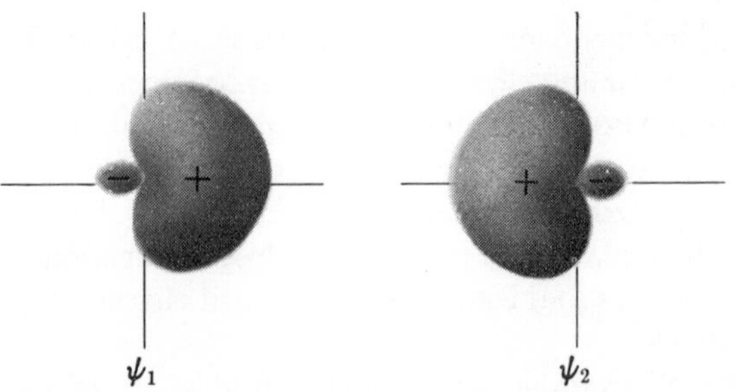

Figure 2-1 *sp hybrids.*

stronger due to increased concentration of electron density along bonding directions between nuclei.

The three hybrid orbitals formed by combining an *s* orbital and two *p* orbitals, designated sp^2, are similar in shape to those shown in Figure 2-1 but are oriented with respect to each other at angles of 120° from each other, thereby lying in a plane. Examples of molecules to which sp^2 bonding has been assigned are BF_3, BCl_3, and BBr_3. These sp^2 hybrid orbitals are also important in molecules and ions containing double bonds—e.g., NO_3^- and HCFO.

Among the most frequently encountered symmetries in chemistry is the tetrahedral, which can result from hybridization of one *s* and three *p* orbitals. The mathematical form for the tetrahedral, or sp^3, hybrids depends on the choice of spatial orientation. We can imagine the nucleus at the center of a cube with p_x, p_y, and p_z orbitals directed toward face centers. If the set of hybrid orbitals is oriented to alternate corners of the cube, the wave functions have a relatively simple form:

$$\psi_1 = \tfrac{1}{2}(\psi_s + \psi_{p_x} + \psi_{p_y} + \psi_{p_z})$$

$$\psi_2 = \tfrac{1}{2}(\psi_s + \psi_{p_x} - \psi_{p_y} - \psi_{p_z})$$

$$\psi_3 = \tfrac{1}{2}(\psi_s - \psi_{p_x} + \psi_{p_y} - \psi_{p_z})$$

$$\psi_4 = \tfrac{1}{2}(\psi_s - \psi_{p_x} - \psi_{p_y} + \psi_{p_z})$$

Whereas the shape of each sp^3 hybrid is somewhat the same as that for an *sp* hybrid, as shown in Figure 2-1, the size of the nonbonding lobe is larger for the sp^3. Figure 2-2 shows schematically the spatial orientation appropriate to sp^3 hybridization. Familiar examples of sp^3 hybridization are NH_4^+, PO_4^{-3}, CCl_4, SiH_4, $SnCl_4$, BF_4^-, and $ZnBr_4^=$. Even nontetrahedral molecules such as NH_3 and H_2O can be considered as examples of sp^3 hybridization. As noted in Section 2-2, bond angles in NH_3 (107.3°) are far from the 90° expected from the valence-bond approach using *p* orbitals directly. If, however, the nitrogen orbitals are first hybridized to sp^3 hybrids and three of these are used for exchange interaction with *s* orbitals of hydrogen, the result is three N—H bonds directed at tetrahedral angles (109.5°). The small discrepancy between the expected tetrahedral angle and the observed value has been attributed to repulsion between the "lone pair" of elec-

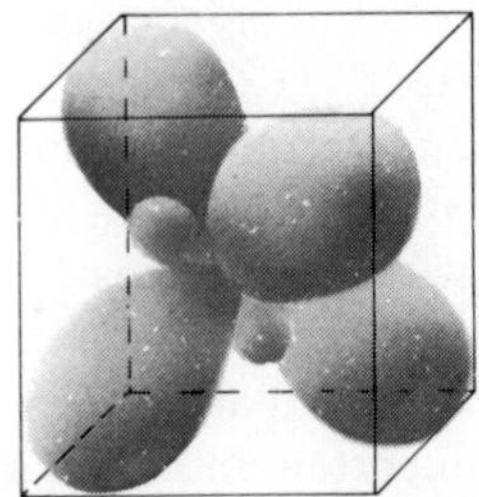

Figure 2-2 *sp^3 hybrids. Note: Each orbital is individually outlined. Total electron density for the set would be spherically symmetric.*

trons in the fourth sp^3 hybrid and the bonding pairs in the other three. The H_2O molecule can be visualized as containing two "lone pairs" of electrons in two of the sp^3 hybrid orbitals. The observed angle of 104.5° is even further from the tetrahedral, perhaps due to increased repulsion by the two "lone pairs."

In general, orbitals can be hybridized successfully only if they are of similar energy. For atoms of low Z, only s and p orbitals are useful for hybridization. For atoms of higher Z, d orbitals may also be available and their inclusion can extend the symmetry possibilities. Perhaps the most important single configuration encountered in *inorganic* chemistry is the octahedral, made available when two d orbitals are mixed with an s and three p orbitals. The spatial distribution of the six hybrid d^2sp^3 orbitals and their relation to the individual atomic orbitals can be seen by considering again a nucleus at the center of a cube. The three mutually perpendicular p orbitals, oriented toward face centers, and the two d orbitals (d_{z^2} and $d_{x^2-y^2}$ of Figure 1-3), similarly directed, mix with the spherically symmetric s orbital to form six hybrid orbitals each directed toward a face center of the cube. These are shown schematically in Figure 2-3. The six wave functions are as follows:

$$\psi_1 = \frac{1}{\sqrt{6}}\psi_s + \frac{1}{\sqrt{2}}\psi_{p_z} + \frac{1}{\sqrt{3}}\psi_{d_z}$$

$$\psi_2 = \frac{1}{\sqrt{6}}\psi_s - \frac{1}{\sqrt{2}}\psi_{p_z} + \frac{1}{\sqrt{3}}\psi_{d_{z^2}}$$

$$\psi_3 = \frac{1}{\sqrt{6}}\psi_s + \frac{1}{\sqrt{2}}\psi_{px} + \frac{1}{\sqrt{12}}\psi_{d_z^2} + \tfrac{1}{2}\psi_{d_{x^2-y^2}}$$

$$\psi_4 = \frac{1}{\sqrt{6}}\psi_s - \frac{1}{\sqrt{2}}\psi_{px} + \frac{1}{\sqrt{12}}\psi_{d_z^2} + \tfrac{1}{2}\psi_{d_{x^2-y^2}}$$

$$\psi_5 = \frac{1}{\sqrt{6}}\psi_s + \frac{1}{\sqrt{2}}\psi_{py} + \frac{1}{\sqrt{12}}\psi_{d_z^2} - \tfrac{1}{2}\psi_{d_{x^2-y^2}}$$

$$\psi_6 = \frac{1}{\sqrt{6}}\psi_s - \frac{1}{\sqrt{2}}\psi_{py} + \frac{1}{\sqrt{12}}\psi_{d_z^2} - \tfrac{1}{2}\psi_{d_{x^2-y^2}}$$

The condition that the orbitals to be hybridized be of approximately equal energy is met by using *d* orbitals having the same principal quantum number as the *s* and *p* or preferably having a principal quantum number one lower. For example, in the case of elements of the first-row transition series [e.g., $Co(NH_3)_6^{+3}$, $Cr(H_2O)_6^{+3}$, $Fe(CN)_6^{-4}$, and $Cr(C_2O_4)_3^{-3}$], octahedral orbitals are formed from 3*d*, 4*s*, and 4*p*. On the other hand, at the right of the periodic table an element, such as iodine in H_5IO_6, may form octahedral orbitals using 5*s*, 5*p*, and 5*d*,

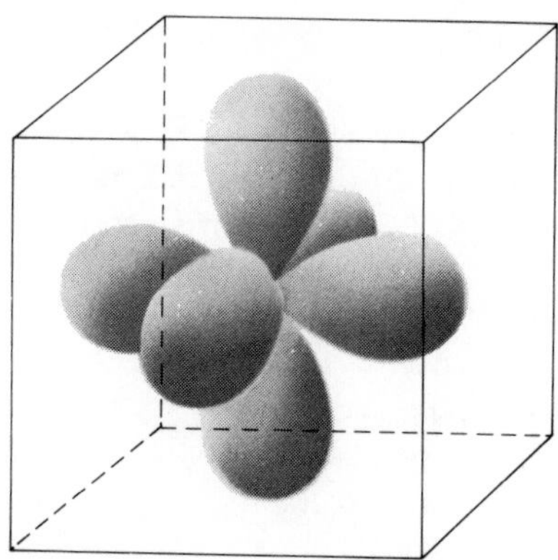

Figure 2-3 *d^2sp^3 hybrids. Note: Each orbital is individually outlined. Total electron density for the set would be spherically symmetric.*

where the $5d$ orbitals have been contracted by greater effective nuclear charge so as to match more nearly the energy of the $5p$ and $5s$.

Inclusion of d orbitals also makes possible square-planar configurations. From Figure 2-3 it can be seen that the elimination of the vertical lobes (z direction) gives four orbitals directed at right angles to each other in the xy plane. Elimination of the vertical lobes can be achieved by omitting from the hybrid set the functions d_{z^2} and p_z. The four resulting dsp^2 hybrid wave functions are

$$\psi_1 = \tfrac{1}{2}\psi_s + \frac{1}{\sqrt{2}}\psi_{px} + \tfrac{1}{2}\psi_{dx^2-y^2}$$

$$\psi_2 = \tfrac{1}{2}\psi_s - \frac{1}{\sqrt{2}}\psi_{px} + \tfrac{1}{2}\psi_{dx^2-y^2}$$

$$\psi_3 = \tfrac{1}{2}\psi_s + \frac{1}{\sqrt{2}}\psi_{py} - \tfrac{1}{2}\psi_{dx^2-y^2}$$

$$\psi_4 = \tfrac{1}{2}\psi_s - \frac{1}{\sqrt{2}}\psi_{py} - \tfrac{1}{2}\psi_{dx^2-y^2}$$

Examples of species to which square-planar configurations have been assigned are: $Ni(CN)_4^{-2}$, $PdCl_4^{-2}$, $AuCl_4^-$, and $Pt(NH_3)_2Cl_2$.

Table 2-1 summarizes the symmetries appropriate to the various hybrid orbitals.

Table 2-1 *Symmetries appropriate to hybrid orbitals*

Hybrid	Symmetry	Example
sp	Linear	$HgCl_2$
sp^2	Trigonal	BCl_3
sp^3	Tetrahedral	CCl_4
dsp^2	Square planar	$AuCl_4^-$
dsp^3	Trigonal bipyramidal	PCl_5
d^2sp^3	Octahedral	$PtCl_6^=$
d^4sp^3	Dodecahedral	$Mo(CN)_8^{-4}$

● 2-4 π Bonds

For the hitherto-considered valence-bond descriptions, the two orbitals undergoing exchange interaction are oriented directly toward each other so that the resultant bond is symmetric about the line joining the two nuclei (there is no angular node). Such bonds are called "sigma" bonds. In certain cases where a σ bond exists between two given atoms, other orbitals may be oriented in such close proximity that additional exchange interaction can occur. The resulting additional bond will in general not be symmetric about the bond axis but will have a nodal plane; it is called a π bond.

As a specific example, let us consider formation of the N_2 molecule. For the nitrogen atom, the electron configuration is $1s^2 2s^2 2p_x^1 2p_y^1 2p_z^1$. Consider two N atoms aligned with the p_x orbitals on the same x axis and the p_y and p_z orbitals parallel one atom to the other. A σ bond is formed by exchange interaction between the p_x orbitals of the two atoms, as shown in Figure 2-4. The shared electron pair is cylindrically symmetric about the x axis—that is, the wave function is the same for a given perpendicular distance r from the x axis independent of the angle r makes within a yz plane.

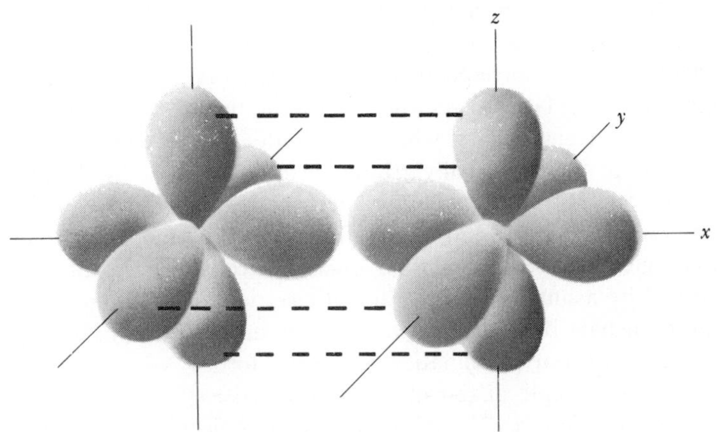

Figure 2-4 *N_2 molecule. Note: Orbitals are schematic as in Figures 2-2 and 2-3.*

Exchange interaction can also occur between the p_z orbitals of the two atoms, leading to a π bond which does not have cylindrical symmetry because there is a nodal plane corresponding to the xy plane. The reason for this is that the wave functions change sign in going along the z axis through the xy plane. Similarly, a second π bond for which the xz plane is a nodal plane is formed by the p_y orbitals of the two atoms. Thus the N_2 molecule can be said to be triply bonded by one σ and two π bonds. It should be added that, although neither of the π bonds by itself has cylindrical symmetry about the bond axis, the combination of the two does in fact lead to electron probability distribution which has cylindrical symmetry.

• 2-5 Resonance

The bonding picture thus far discussed implies (1) pure covalent binding and (2) integral bond order. Pure covalent binding means equal sharing of electron pairs; integral bond order means that a pair of electrons is either shared or not. In fact, most real examples cannot be satisfactorily described within these two limitations but require descriptions which may be approximated by judicious combinations of simpler wave functions. This procedure, called "resonance," has proved to be useful in giving qualitative interpretations of a variety of observed phenomena.

An example of so-called *ionic-covalent resonance* is the complex ion CrF_6^{-3}. Two limiting possibilities present themselves, one of which is strictly ionic and corresponds to Cr^{+3} and $6F^-$, while the other, strictly covalent, corresponds to $Cr^{-3}(F^\circ)_6$. (The peculiar charge assignment of the latter arises from the assumption of equal sharing of six pairs of electrons, each of which contributes on the average one negative charge to the initially tripositive chromium.) As Pauling has pointed out, it is improbable for energetic reasons that any atom in a compound will vary from electrical neutrality by more than one unit of charge. This requirement of "essential electrical neutrality" can be satisfied by assuming that the actual electrical distribution in CrF_6^{-3} is intermediate between the two extremes and in fact can be approximated by a linear combination of the two forms.

An example of so-called *bond order resonance* may occur in the complex ion $Fe(CN)_6^{-4}$. Although essential electrical neutrality may be achieved by postulating resonance between an ionic form (Fe^{++} and $6CN^-$) and a covalent form $Fe^{-4}(CN^\circ)_6$, it may also be achieved through bond order resonance by allowing "back donation" of electronic charge from *d* orbitals of the iron to orbitals made available on carbon atoms. For orbitals to become available on the carbon, one of the π bonds originally between the carbon and the nitrogen must be broken with the pair of electrons moving to the nitrogen as a lone pair. The *p* orbital of the carbon can then accommodate electron pair density from the iron, thereby shifting negative charge outward from the iron to the nitrogen. Two of the bond order resonance forms can be written

$$(CN)_5Fe^{(-4)}\text{—}C\equiv N\!: \qquad \text{and} \qquad (CN)_5Fe^{(-3)}\!=\!C\!=\!\ddot{N}\!:^{(-1)}$$

A similar process can occur with the other CN groups sufficient to establish essential neutrality. In the first of the above canonical (or resonance) forms, the σ bond shown between the Fe and the carbon represents electron exchange between an *sp* hybrid on carbon and a d^2sp^3 hybrid on iron. This same bond is retained as the σ bond between Fe and carbon in the second canonical form. The new bond in the second form is a π bond formed by electron interaction between one of the filled *d* orbitals on iron (d_{xy}, d_{yz}, or d_{zx}) and a made-available *p* orbital on the carbon. This interaction is geometrically possible because, for example, a d_{zx} orbital on the iron is favorably situated to exchange with a p_z orbital on the carbon.

In order that an individual canonical form make any significant contribution (i.e., bear any significant resemblance) to the actual molecule, certain criteria must be met. The canonical form in question must not differ from the other forms in the position of the nuclei; it must be of energy comparable to that of the other forms; it must have the same number of unpaired electrons as the other canonical forms.

• 2-6 Molecular Orbitals

Conceptually more appealing than the valence-bond approach is that of molecular orbitals. In this method, the presence of more than one nucleus generates orbitals which are characteristic of the molecule as a whole. Atomic orbitals as such disappear, and hence the mysterious exchange interaction and resonance vanish. The build-up of a molecule can then be described by: (1) fixing the nuclei at their equilibrium sites, (2) constructing molecular orbitals for the electrons, and (3) feeding in the appropriate number of electrons to the available orbitals in order of increasing energy.

Two methods are generally available for setting up the required molecular orbitals. In one of these, called the "united atom" method, a hypothetical nucleus containing all the nuclear charge for the final molecule is gradually separated into component atoms, passing through the nuclear configuration corresponding to the molecule. From the energy levels of the two limiting situations (united atom vs. isolated atoms), reasonable guesses can be made of the relative energies and symmetries of the molecular levels. This procedure has been used only for the simplest of cases.

More frequently used is the LCAO method, in which the required molecular orbitals are derived by linear combination of atomic orbitals. Justification for this is that for the part of the electric distribution lying close to a nucleus the wave function is much like that of the isolated atom. In the region between two nuclei the molecular orbital bears some resemblance to both atomic functions. Mathematically, the setting up of molecular orbitals by LCAO can be represented as follows:

$$\psi_{\text{M.O.}} = C[a\psi_1 + (1 - a^2)^{1/2}\psi_2]$$

where C is a normalizing factor and a is a parameter ranging from 0 to 1 which weights the relative contribution of atomic orbitals ψ_1 and ψ_2 to the molecular orbital $\psi_{\text{M.O.}}$. a^2 gives the relative electron density in atomic orbital ψ_1 and is equal to $\frac{1}{2}$ when the final molecular orbital is composed equally of ψ_1 and ψ_2. By using the weighting factors a and $(1 - a^2)^{1/2}$, the normalizing factor C is very nearly equal to one and, in fact, is identically one if cross terms $\psi_1\psi_2$ are negligible compared to ${\psi_1}^2$ and ${\psi_2}^2$. For convenience C is omitted in the following discussion. When ψ_1 and ψ_2 are combined, *two* molecular orbitals are obtained. The other one is of the form

$$\psi^*_{\text{M.O.}} = (1 - a^2)^{1/2}\psi_1 - a\psi_2$$

Whereas $\psi_{\text{M.O.}}$ concentrates electron density between the nuclei and is called a bonding orbital, $\psi^*_{\text{M.O.}}$ depletes electron density from the internuclear region and is called an antibonding orbital. An asterisk is usually used for the antibonding orbital, and always an antibonding orbital is higher in energy than the corresponding bonding one.

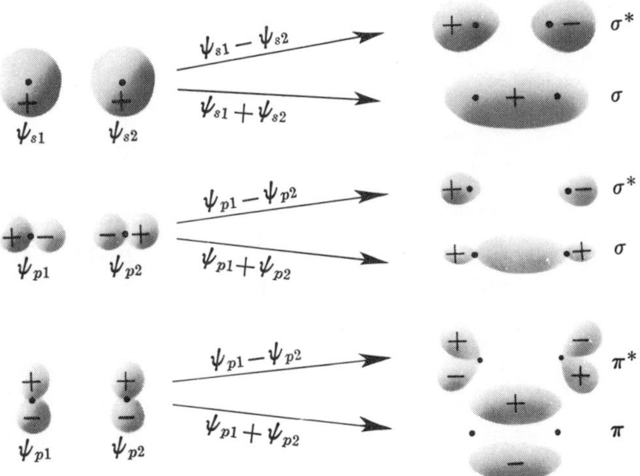

Figure 2-5 *Formation of molecular orbitals from atomic orbitals.*

Molecular orbitals corresponding to cylindrical symmetry about the bond axis are designated as σ orbitals, those leading to nodal planes through the bond axis as π orbitals. As an illustration, *s* atomic orbitals can give rise only to σ and σ^* orbitals, schematic representation of which is given in Figure 2-5. *p* orbitals, depending on relative orientation, can give rise to σ and σ^* or π and π^*.

The O_2 molecule is a good illustration of the successful application of molecular-orbital theory to a case where valence-bond theory fails. The electron population of an isolated oxygen atom is $1s^2 2s^2 2p_x{}^1 2p_y{}^1 2p_z{}^2$. In the molecule, it is assumed that the inner-shell electrons (here just the two sets of 1*s*) remain undisturbed from their initial atomic orbital distribution. The other twelve electrons occupy molecular orbitals whose formation is schematically represented in Figure 2-6. The two 2*s* orbitals combine to give one bonding and one antibonding orbital of σ symmetry. Likewise the two *p* orbitals that are directed along the bond axis (here arbitrarily chosen as p_x) combine to give one bonding and one antibonding orbital of σ symmetry. The pairs of *p* orbitals perpendicular to the bond axis each give rise to a bonding and an antibonding π orbital. Because the p_y and p_z directions are equivalent, the bonding orbitals derived therefrom are of the same

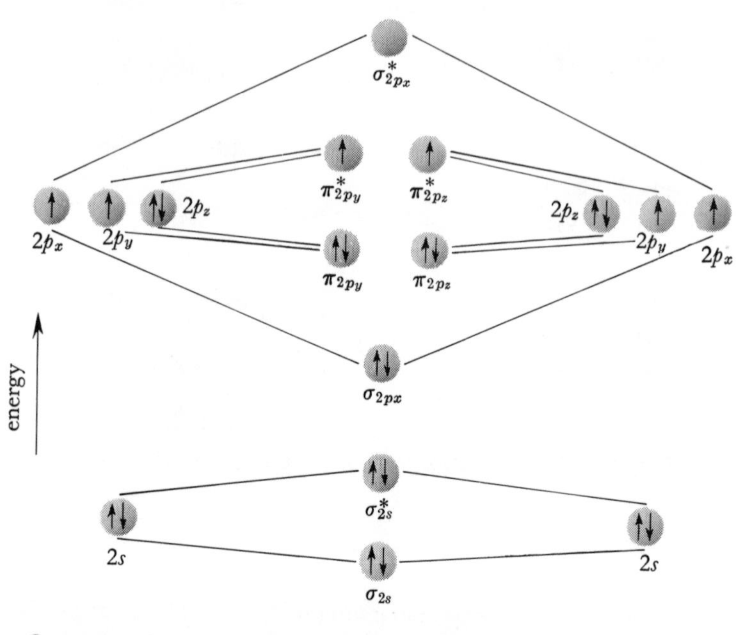

Figure 2-6 *Correlation diagram for O_2.*

energy (degenerate). Similarly, the antibonding π orbitals are degenerate.

In assigning electron population, the Pauli principle permits no more than one pair of spin-coupled electrons per molecular orbital. Five pairs can be accommodated in the five lowest-lying levels shown in Figure 2-6. For the remaining two electrons, two degenerate orbitals ($\pi^*_{p_y}$ and $\pi^*_{p_z}$) are next in line. To reduce electron repulsion, it is energetically favorable for the electrons to remain uncoupled and occupy separate orbitals. Thus the final picture is consistent with the observation that O_2 is paramagnetic to the extent of two uncoupled spins.

In the molecular orbital picture, bond order can be defined as half the number of bonding electrons in excess over antibonding. Thus Figure 2-6 shows O_2 to have eight bonding and four antibonding electrons, or a bond order of two. This is consistent with the experimentally observed bond length and bond strength. N_2, on the other hand, for which the orbitals of Figure 2-6 are also applicable, has no electrons in the $\pi^*_{p_y}$ or $\pi^*_{p_z}$ orbitals; its bond order is three. F_2 has a pair of electrons in each of the π^*_p orbitals; its bond order is unity. These bond orders are consistent with the bond energies (kcal per mole): N_2, 225; O_2, 118; F_2, 36.

Examples of application of molecular orbital analysis to more complex species are given by the octahedral complexes of the transition elements. Let us consider CrF_6^{-3}, for which a correlation diagram is given in Figure 2-7. On the left side of the diagram is shown the atomic orbital population for the ion Cr^{+3}. In the isolated Cr^{+3} ion, the five d orbitals are equivalent and contain three unpaired electrons. The right side of the diagram shows six filled p orbitals, one from each of six

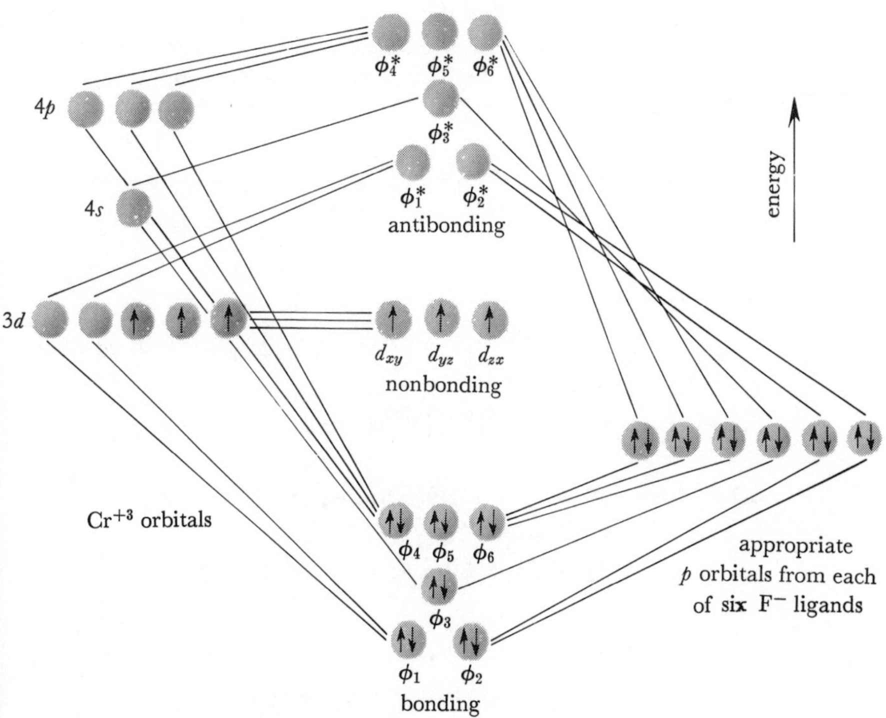

Figure 2-7 *Correlation diagram for CrF_6^{-3}.*

isolated fluoride ions, which are to be used in forming molecular orbitals. Assuming octahedral symmetry for the complex, bonding molecular orbitals must have directional properties which concentrate charge in the regions between the nuclei. If the coordinate system is fixed with origin at the chromium nucleus, the bonding directions can be represented as $+x$, $-x$, $+y$, $-y$, $+z$, and $-z$. Chromium orbitals that are useful in forming molecular orbitals in these directions are ψ_{4p_x}, ψ_{4p_y}, ψ_{4p_z} (directed along the axes), ψ_{4s} (spherically symmetric), ψ_{3d_z} (concentrated along the z axis and in the xy plane), and $\psi_{3d_{x^2-y^2}}$ (concentrated along the x and y axes). The three remaining $3d$ orbitals of the chromium have nodes along the axes (cf. Figure 1-3) and are not useful in forming molecular orbitals directly along the axes. The wave functions for the molecular orbitals are approximated by taking a linear combination of one of the chromium orbitals and as many fluoride orbitals as overlap it appreciably. To simplify the writing of the wave functions the p orbitals of the fluorides will be assumed to be oriented with the positive lobes directed to the chromium. These fluoride orbitals will be designated as ψ_x, ψ_{-x}, ψ_y, ψ_{-y}, ψ_z, and ψ_{-z}, where the subscript denotes the direction of the F^- relative to the chromium.

The molecular orbitals are:

$$\phi_1 = c\psi_{3d_z^2} + (1 - c^2)^{1/2}(\tfrac{1}{12})^{1/2}[-\psi_x - \psi_{-x} - \psi_y - \psi_{-y} + 2\psi_z + 2\psi_{-z}]$$

$$\phi_1^* = (1 - c^2)^{1/2}\psi_{3d_z^2} - c(\tfrac{1}{12})^{1/2}[-\psi_x - \psi_{-x} - \psi_y - \psi_{-y} + 2\psi_z + 2\psi_{-z}]$$

$$\phi_2 = c\psi_{3d_{x^2-y^2}} + (1 - c^2)^{1/2}(\tfrac{1}{4})^{1/2}[\psi_x + \psi_{-x} - \psi_y - \psi_{-y}]$$

$$\phi_2^* = (1 - c^2)^{1/2}\psi_{3d_{x^2-y^2}} - c(\tfrac{1}{4})^{1/2}[\psi_x + \psi_{-x} - \psi_y - \psi_{-y}]$$

$$\phi_3 = a\psi_{4s} + (1 - a^2)^{1/2}(\tfrac{1}{6})^{1/2}[\psi_x + \psi_{-x} + \psi_y + \psi_{-y} + \psi_z + \psi_{-z}]$$

$$\phi_3^* = (1 - a^2)^{1/2}\psi_{4s} - a(\tfrac{1}{6})^{1/2}[\psi_x + \psi_{-x} + \psi_y + \psi_{-y} + \psi_z + \psi_{-z}]$$

$$\phi_4 = b\psi_{4p_x} + (1 - b^2)^{1/2}(\tfrac{1}{2})^{1/2}[\psi_x - \psi_{-x}]$$

$$\phi_4^* = (1 - b^2)^{1/2}\psi_{4p_x} - b(\tfrac{1}{2})^{1/2}[\psi_x - \psi_{-x}]$$

$$\phi_5 = b\psi_{4p_y} + (1 - b^2)^{1/2}(\tfrac{1}{2})^{1/2}[\psi_y - \psi_{-y}]$$

$$\phi_5^* = (1 - b^2)^{1/2}\psi_{4p_y} - b(\tfrac{1}{2})^{1/2}[\psi_y - \psi_{-y}]$$

$$\phi_6 = b\psi_{4p_z} + (1 - b^2)^{1/2}(\tfrac{1}{2})^{1/2}[\psi_z - \psi_{-z}]$$

$$\phi_6^* = (1 - b^2)^{1/2}\psi_{4p_z} - b(\tfrac{1}{2})^{1/2}[\psi_z - \psi_{-z}]$$

In these equations, the positive constants a, b, and c are selected so as to minimize the energy. Zero values of these constants would imply bonding orbitals that are completely concentrated on the ligands; unit values, on the central atom. Equal weighting of Cr and F orbitals would correspond to the case where $a = b = c = \sqrt{\frac{1}{2}}$. The problem has not been solved completely but because fluorine is more electronegative than chromium, one would expect the actual values to lie between zero and $\sqrt{\frac{1}{2}}$.

The final electron assignment shown in Figure 2-7 is consistent with the observation that the CrF_6^{-3} complex is paramagnetic to the extent of three unpaired electrons. In CrF_6^{-3}, the three unpaired electrons are accommodated in the three degenerate nonbonding orbitals d_{xy}, d_{yz}, d_{zx}. The same correlation diagram could in principle be used to describe other transition-element complexes and so lead to a prediction of their magnetic behavior. For elements preceding chromium the prediction is straightforward; for example, K_3VF_6 has a paramagnetic moment of 2.79 Bohr magnetons. However, for the elements following chromium difficulties appear as the number of electrons increases. The problem arises because additional electrons can be accommodated either by pairing in the nonbonding orbitals or without pairing in the antibonding orbitals. The choice between these two possibilities depends on the relative energy required to overcome repulsion by another electron in the same orbital (of the order of 40 to 50 kcal per mole, depending on the case in question) compared to the energy increment from the nonbonding to the antibonding state. As we shall see later (Section 2-9), the energy increment can be determined by examination of absorption spectra and depending on the specific case can have values as high as some 75 kcal per mole.

The complex FeF_6^{-3} contains two electrons more than shown for CrF_6^{-3} in Figure 2-7. If the electron-pairing energy were small enough, these two additional electrons could be accommodated in the nonbonding orbitals leading to a single unpaired electron. The paramagnetic moment of 5.88 Bohr magnetons observed for the compound $(NH_4)_3FeF_6$ indicates five unpaired electrons. Therefore, the conclusion is that for FeF_6^{-3} the energy difference between the nonbonding states and the ϕ_1^*, ϕ_2^* orbitals is smaller than the electron-pairing energy.

The energy difference between the nonbonding and antibonding states is strongly dependent on the nature of the ligands attached to the central atom. Substitution of cyanide for fluoride gives the complex $Fe(CN)_6^{-3}$, which has an observed paramagnetic moment of about 2.3 to 2.4 Bohr magnetons, close to a one-unpaired electron value calculated by spin-only plus some orbital contribution. Apparently, in this case, the three nonbonding orbitals accommodate two pairs and one unpaired electron. Cyanide ligands serve to split the bonding and antibonding orbitals more widely, and hence the energy increment between nonbonding and antibonding orbitals is greater than the pairing energy.

Why should CN produce a greater splitting in the molecular orbitals than does F? As already mentioned in Section 2-5, equal sharing of electrons between central atom and ligand (corresponding in the present picture to $a = b = c = \sqrt{\frac{1}{2}}$) concentrates too much negative charge at the iron atom. In FeF_6^{-3}, this is avoided by constructing the molecular orbitals to favor the more electronegative fluorine (reduced values of a, b, and c). When this is done, the antibonding states ϕ_1^* and ϕ_2^* become closer to the atomic states $\psi_{3d_{z^2}}$ and $\psi_{3d_{x^2-y^2}}$ and nearer in energy to d_{xy}, d_{yz}, and d_{zx}. However, as also mentioned in Section 2-5, for the cyanide complex, charge can be shifted from the iron to the ligand by "back donation" to form π bonds. Because of this charge shift, somewhat larger values of a, b, and c are permitted, and there is a resultant greater splitting of the various types of molecular orbitals. However, introduction of the "back donation" complicates the whole picture by involving the nonbonding orbitals in molecular orbital formation. The d_{xy}, d_{yz}, d_{zx} orbitals can be combined with ligand orbitals in much the same way as discussed in the valence-bond treatment, giving three new bonding and three new antibonding orbitals in place of the previously nonbonding ones.

• 2-7 Three-Center Bonds

In Section 2-6 molecular orbitals were developed which extended over a number of nuclei. In the cases considered, the number of electrons in bonding orbitals was at least sufficient for the number of bonds in a classical structure. There are certain compounds—in particular, the boron hydrides—for which classical structures cannot be drawn. For these it is especially fortunate that there are molecular orbitals which are spread over more than two nuclei. As a consequence, there is no special requirement that two electrons be shared between pairs of adjacent atoms, and the term "electron deficiency" sometimes used for these compounds has little meaning.

The molecule B_2H_6 contains two boron atoms and four hydrogen atoms in the same plane, as indicated in Figure 2-8. The other two hydrogen atoms are located above and below this plane, more or less bridging the borons. The upper lobe B^I—H—B^{II} constitutes a molecular orbital encompassing three nuclei and is called a "three-center" orbital, or, sometimes, a "banana bond." A pair of electrons is accommodated in this orbital and another pair in the otherwise identical lower lobe B^I—H—B^{II}. This three-center molecular orbital can be approximated as a linear combination of an sp^3 hybrid from each boron atom and the $1s$ of the hydrogen atom.

$$\psi = \frac{a}{2}\psi^{I}_{sp^3} + \sqrt{1 - a^2/2}\,\psi_{1s} + \frac{a}{2}\psi^{II}_{sp^3}$$

Each boron contributes two of its sp^3 hybrids to "banana bond" formation, leaving the other two for binding the terminal hydrogen atoms by conventional σ bonds.

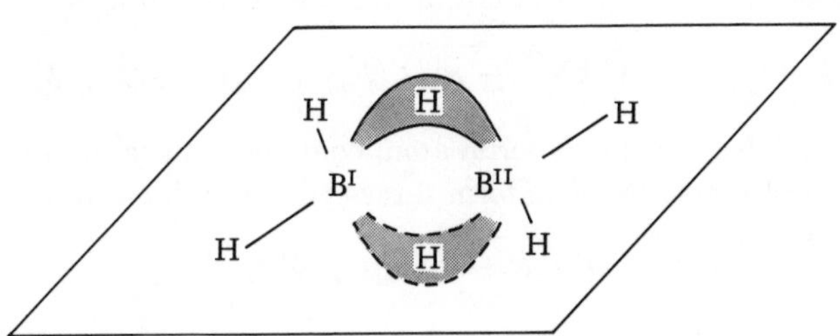

Figure 2-8 *Diborane.*

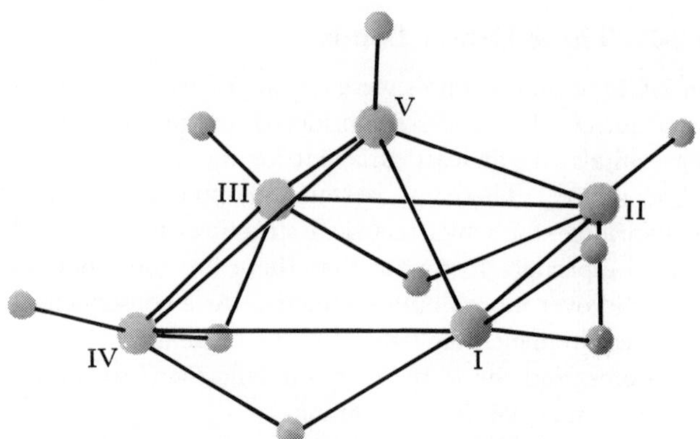

Figure 2-9 B_5H_9.

The higher boron hydrides can be treated similarly except that additional types of multicenter bonds may have to be utilized. For example, B_5H_9, shown in Figure 2-9, has a five-membered boron framework with one five-center and two three-center orbitals. The orbitals arise in the following way. Assuming sp^3 hybridization for each of the four boron atoms in the square, one sp^3 hybrid orbital can be used to bind a terminal hydrogen atom, two are used to form banana bonds with bridge hydrogens to other boron atoms, and the fourth is contributed to the boron framework. Of the three boron electrons, one is used for the terminal hydrogen, one for the two banana bonds together, and one for the framework. The apex boron atom is bonded to a terminal hydrogen by an sp hybrid orbital. The other sp orbital, along with the two p orbitals (and two electrons), are contributed to the framework. From the sp orbital of the apex boron atom and the sp^3 hybrids of the base boron atoms, a five-center orbital arises:

$$\psi = \frac{a}{\sqrt{2}}\psi_{sp} + \tfrac{1}{2}\sqrt{1 - a^2/2}\,(\psi^{\mathrm{I}}_{sp^3} + \psi^{\mathrm{II}}_{sp^3} + \psi^{\mathrm{III}}_{sp^3} + \psi^{\mathrm{IV}}_{sp^3})$$

The p orbitals of the apex boron atom combine with sp^3 hybrids of alternate base boron atoms to form three-centered orbitals of the type

$$\psi = \frac{a}{\sqrt{2}}\psi_{p_x} + \tfrac{1}{2}\sqrt{2 - a^2}\,(\psi^{\mathrm{I}}_{sp^3} - \psi^{\mathrm{III}}_{sp^3})$$

$$\psi = \frac{a}{\sqrt{2}}\psi_{p_y} + \tfrac{1}{2}\sqrt{2 - a^2}\,(\psi^{\mathrm{II}}_{sp^3} - \psi^{\mathrm{IV}}_{sp^3})$$

• 2-8 Ligand Field Theory

In the preceding sections the discussion of chemical bonds was based on the concept of electron sharing with adjustable parameters to take into account differences in electronegativity. Under certain circumstances it may be preferable to approach the problem from the opposite extreme—that is, to assume that the complex is constructed of ions and/or dipoles and then to introduce parameters to take into account deviations from a simple, point-charge, Coulombic interaction. Such deviations are: departures from spherical symmetry of ions such as Cr^{+3} which contain partially filled electron shells, polarization of atoms by localized charges on neighboring atoms, delocalization of electrons (e.g., covalent bonding). All these deviations which lower the energy of the system can be said to contribute to the bonding.

The problem of a nonspherical ion under the influence of a nonspherical electric field is of major importance in solid-state phenomena, and the method for treating it is usually referred to as "crystal field theory." The essence of the method is to use group theory as applied to symmetry operations to deduce the splitting of atomic energy levels due to symmetry properties of the electric fields in the crystal. The term "ligand field theory" is applied to a similar procedure except that the effective field is considered to be imposed not by the whole crystal but by the ligands which immediately surround the atom in question. In the latter case, covalent forces may be more important than the Coulombic ones. From group theory, it is not possible to obtain the magnitude of the energy level splitting. It was hoped originally that the energy level splitting could be calculated from a simple Coulombic model, but now it seems clear that such calculations are only rough approximations. Instead, relative energies are deduced by a semi-empirical approach which is based on spectral observation.

In the following treatment we limit ourselves to a qualitative discussion of the form of the splitting and of periodic trends in the splitting parameters. For these purposes it is convenient to have some familiarity with the symbolism generally used in applications of group theory. The small letters a, b, e, and t, for example, generally refer to one-electron descriptions (orbitals, wave functions, or the like) classified according to symmetry properties. (The capital letter designations A, B, E, and T refer to multi-electron states of corresponding symmetry.) These designations give information as to the degeneracy number—that is, the number of ways of producing the same energy. A state designated as *a* or *b*, is nondegenerate and corresponds to but a single wave function or orbital. States *e* and *t* are twofold and threefold degenerate, respectively.

Thus, for example, two independent wave functions that are identical with respect to the symmetry of a specified field are twofold degenerate and may be designated by *e*. The difference between *a* and *b* is that the former implies that there is no change of sign in the wave function in rotating through $2\pi/n$ about an *n*-fold axis of rotation. (An *n*-fold axis is one that produces *n* indistinguishable configurations per revolution.) With *b*, however, there is change of sign. Further symmetry distinctions may be made through use of subscripts. As usually employed, *g* (for *gerade*) implies no change in the sign of the wave function on inversion through the origin—that is, replacement of positive coordinate positions by equivalent negative ones; *u* (for *ungerade*) indicates that the sign changes. The subscripts 1 and 2 usually designate differences with respect to mirror planes.

What happens in an octahedral field to an atom, such as Ti^{+3}, containing a single electron in a *d* orbital? The octahedral field can be visualized as being produced by bringing six negative ions in along the coordinate axes toward the metal atom at the origin. In field-free space, the five *d* orbitals are degenerate, but once the ligands have been brought up a field is imposed which may remove some of the degeneracy. Electrical repulsion between the *d* electron and the negative ligands will raise the energy in the case of a *d* orbital directed along the axes and lower the energy in case the *d* orbital is concentrated between the axes. There are two *d* orbitals, the d_{z^2} and the $d_{x^2-y^2}$, which will be raised in energy and three, d_{xy}, d_{yz}, and d_{zx}, which will be lowered. The "center of gravity" of the set remains unchanged, so that the doublet rises by $\frac{3}{2}$ as much as the triplet drops.

Figure 2-10 is a schematic diagram of the splitting process. The two orbitals of the upper set (sometimes called $d\gamma$) are often described by the symmetry designation e_g and the three orbitals of the lower set (sometimes called $d\epsilon$) by the symmetry designation t_{2g}. By convention, the total splitting between the t_{2g} and e_g orbitals is designated as $10Dq$, so in a sense Dq is a measure of the strength of the ligand field. Values of Dq can be obtained from observations on absorption spectra. In general, the absorption spectrum of a transition-metal complex ion contains a strong band in the ultraviolet (which is attributed to the energy required to transfer charge between ligand and central atom) and one or more much weaker bands on the long-

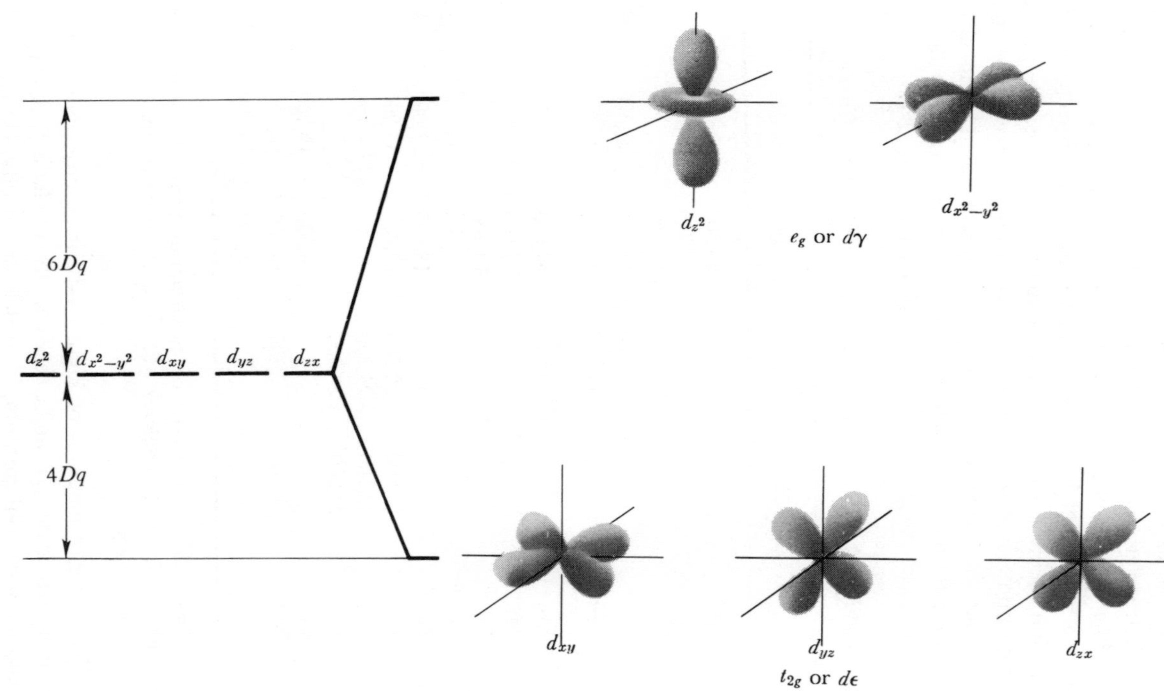

Figure 2-10 *Splitting of d orbitals in an octahedral field.*

wavelength side of the charge-transfer band. The weak absorptions are referred to as ligand field bands and are attributed to energy required to transfer an electron from a lower ligand field level to a higher.

The energy splitting varies from case to case. It seems to depend on a number of factors including the following: the charge of the central ion, being greater the greater the ionic charge; the principal quantum number of the *d* level involved, being greater for 4*d* and 5*d* than for 3*d*; the nature of the ligand, being dependent on its charge-density distribution and polarizability. Representative values for the ligand field parameter 10*Dq* are given in Table 2-2.

Table 2-2 *Values of 10Dq in wave numbers (in* cm^{-1}*)* [a]

		$6Br^-$	$6Cl^-$	$6H_2O$	$6NH_3$	$6CN^-$
$3d^1$	Ti^{+3}			20,300		
$3d^2$	V^{+3}			17,700		
$3d^3$	V^{++}			12,600		
	Cr^{+3}		13,600	17,400	21,600	26,300
$4d^3$	Mo^{+3}		19,200			
$3d^4$	Cr^{++}			13,900		
	Mn^{+3}			21,000		
$3d^5$	Mn^{++}			7,800		
	Fe^{+3}			13,700		
$3d^6$	Fe^{++}			10,400		33,000
	Co^{+3}			18,600	23,000	34,000
$4d^6$	Rh^{+3}	18,900	20,300	27,000	33,900	
$5d^6$	Ir^{+3}	23,100	24,900			
	Pt^{+4}	24,000	29,000			
$3d^7$	Co^{++}			9,300	10,100	
$3d^8$	Ni^{++}	7,000	7,300	8,500	10,800	
$3d^9$	Cu^{++}			12,600	15,100	

[a] These values, which are from spectral transitions, are strictly equal to 10*Dq* only for octahedral complexes. For d^4 and d^9 there are major distortions which are not corrected for.

The energy diagram of Figure 2-10 is strictly applicable only to a one-electron case. It can be used equally well for a d^1 configuration and also for a d^6 configuration, in which one orbital contains a spin pair and the other four, unpaired electrons. (A d^6 configuration is equivalent to a d^5 plus d^1 configuration, where the d^5 constitutes a complete orbital set with $L=0$.) The diagram of Figure 2-10 can also be treated as though it were an electron-filling diagram for other d^n configurations. Let us consider d^4. If no spin-pairing occurs, four orbitals will be needed. Three of these will be of the t_{2g} set and the fourth of the e_g. This configuration is the ground state and its symmetry is E. That this is the symmetry can be seen by considering the d^4 configuration to be the totally symmetric set d^5 plus an "electron hole," which can be either in d_{z^2} or $d_{x^2-y^2}$, thereby conferring the e_g symmetry on the whole state. For the excited state, one of the electrons must be transferred from d_{xy}, d_{yz}, or d_{zx} to the vacant d_{z^2} or $d_{x^2-y^2}$. The vacancy now resides in one of the t_{2g} orbitals and bestows t_{2g} symmetry on the excited state, making it T_2. Just as d^6 is equivalent to d^1, d^9 can be considered equivalent to d^4. Since d^9 can be thought of as d^{10} plus an "electron hole," the ground state would have symmetry E (corresponding to six electrons in d_{xy}, d_{yz}, d_{zx} and three electrons in d_{z^2} and $d_{x^2-y^2}$), and the excited state would have symmetry T_2 (five electrons in d_{xy}, d_{yz}, d_{zx} and four in d_{z^2} and $d_{x^2-y^2}$).

The relation between ground state and excited state is summarized in Figure 2-11 for the configurations d^1, d^4, d^6, d^9. The diagrams indicate that in all these cases there is a ligand field transition of energy $10Dq$ and also that the ground state of the ion in an octahedral field is lower than if the ion were spherical or were in a spherical field of comparable strength. Thus, for a d^1 ion, for example, the lowering of the

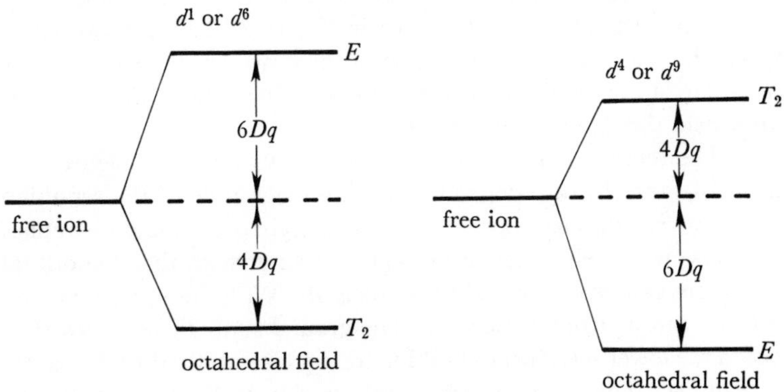

Figure 2-11 *Splitting diagrams for d^1 or d^6 and d^4 or d^9.*

energy is $4Dq$. For Ti^{+3} surrounded by H_2O, this would correspond to roughly 24 kcal. This energy, called "ligand field stabilization energy," arises simply because the nonspherical Ti^{+3} ion can orient favorably in the octahedral field of H_2O molecules. It should be emphasized that this stabilization energy is in addition to all other interaction energies between Ti^{+3} and H_2O. To keep things in proper perspective, the total hydration energy of Ti^{+3} is approximately 1000 kcal.

The complete treatment of the d^2 configuration would require solution of the problem of a coupled-electron system in an electric field, but it can be approximated by extension of the one-electron-orbital method used above. The ground state is formed by placing the two electrons in two of the three t_{2g} orbitals. Since there are three ways of doing this, the state is triply degenerate (and is labeled T_1).

For the excited states, several possibilities exist, unlike the single-electron cases discussed above. For one thing, one electron may be placed in each of the upper two e_g orbitals, in which case we have a non-degenerate state (symmetry A_2). Alternatively, there may be one electron in each of the two sets of orbitals. However, this is not a single state, since electron repulsion is different depending on which orbitals are used in each set. There are six ways of distributing the electrons. Three of these will be degenerate and have large electron-electron repulsion—e.g., $d_{x^2-y^2}$ and d_{xy}. The other three possibilities are also degenerate, but have minimum electron-electron repulsion—e.g., d_{z^2} and d_{xy}. The first, higher energy, set has symmetry T_1; the second, T_2. Figure 2-12 shows the splitting diagram for d^2, which also holds for d^7. For these configurations, electron-electron repulsions are important even for the free ion. This is shown in Figure 2-12 by the two levels on the left. Actually, the separation of these two levels relative to the magnitude of the ligand field strength determines whether in the octahedral field the A_2 or T_1 lies higher.

The relative spacings of the energy levels shown in Figure 2-12 (except A_2 and T_2) are dependent on the magnitude of the repulsion energy between the electrons. The extreme right of the diagram applies to the case where electronic repulsion is weak enough that the orbital populations can be considered to be integral. With this approximation the levels can be fixed as follows. The ground state T_1 with two electrons in the lower set of orbitals of Figure 2-10 is stabilized to the extent of $2 \times 4\,Dq$. The T_2 state with one electron in each set is "stabilized" by $4Dq$ and "destabilized" by $6Dq$, giving a net rise of $2Dq$. The A_2

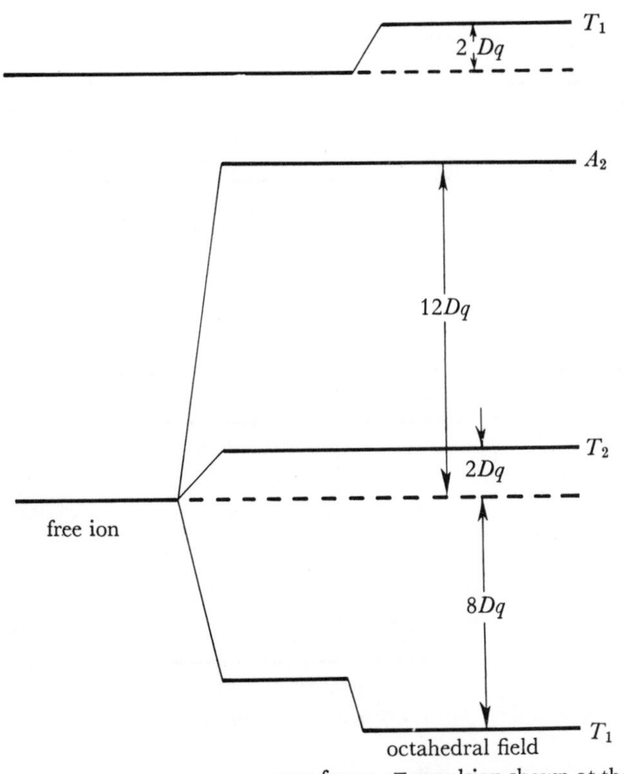

Figure 2-12 *Splitting diagram for d^2 or d^7.*

state has both electrons in the upper orbitals and hence its energy is raised by $2 \times 6\ Dq$. The upper T_1 state has one electron in each set for a net rise of $2Dq$. For real cases, the T_1 states are pulled closer together by an amount depending on the intensity of the electronic repulsion.

Figure 2-13 shows the splitting diagram for a d^3 or d^8 configuration. Again there is splitting in the free ion, as shown on the left of the diagram. In the octahedral field, the lowest state of the d^3 corresponds to having the three electrons in the lower orbitals d_{xy}, d_{yz}, d_{zx} and hence a stabilization energy of $12Dq$. Its symmetry is A_2 (nondegenerate). Promotion of one electron to an upper orbital leads to two different states, depending on electron-electron repulsion. For both these

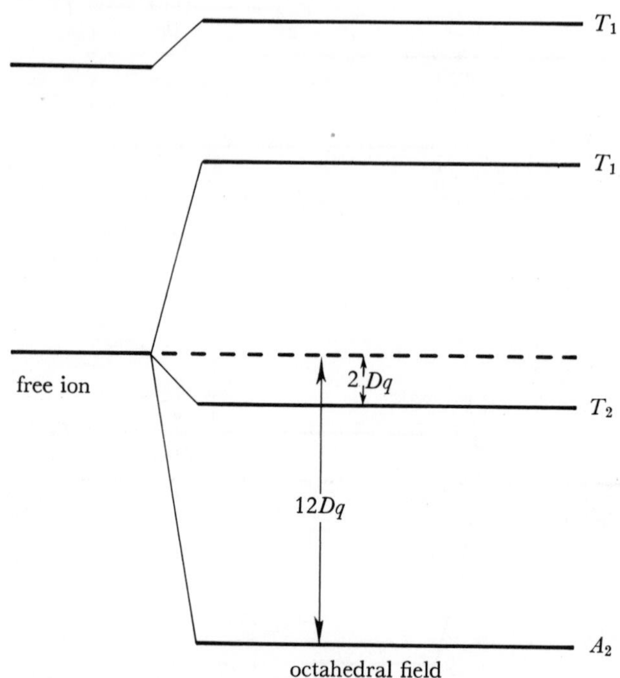

Figure 2-13 *Splitting diagram for d^3 or d^8.*

states the ligand field stabilization energy is $2Dq$, but the T_1 state lies above the T_2 by an amount dependent upon the electron repulsion. The highest energy state is also T_1, and in our approximation corresponds to two electrons in upper orbitals. Its position on the diagram depends on the amount of electron repulsion.

The previous discussions have tacitly assumed that electron spin-pairing is minimal. For example, the d^6 configuration has four unpaired electrons and one pair in the five orbitals. However, in the hydrated Co^{+3} ion, which is a d^6 configuration, the magnetic moment indicates three pairs of electrons. On a ligand field basis, the reason for this is that the ligand field stabilization energy exceeds the electron-pairing repulsion energy. This can be seen by reference to the electron-filling diagram of Figure 2-10. If six electrons are spread out to give maximum spin, the net stabilization is $4 \times 4\ Dq - 2 \times 6\ Dq = 4Dq$. If, however, the six electrons are all placed in the lower set giving minimum spin, the stabilization is $6 \times 4\,Dq = 24Dq$. The low-spin case seems to be favored by $20Dq$, or approximately 110 kcal. However, the low-spin configuration has two electron pairs more than the high-spin configuration, which introduces a repulsion energy of some 80 to 100 kcal. Thus, on balance, the low-spin case is favored and Figure 2-11 does not apply to low-spin complexes of Co^{+3} such as $Co(H_2O)_6{}^{+3}$, $Co(NH_3)_6{}^{+3}$, $Co(CN)_6{}^{-3}$, etc. It does apply to $CoF_6{}^{-3}$.

In cases where low-spin configurations obtain, the splitting diagram used should correspond to the orbitals populated. Thus, for low-spin complexes of Co^{+3}, Fe^{++}, Fe^{+3}, etc., one uses the d^3 diagram, and the absorption spectra of such complexes strongly resemble those of $Cr^{+3}(d^3)$. Other cases where low-spin configurations obtain are frequently observed with complex ions containing transition elements of the $4d$ and $5d$ sequences. As noted previously, ligand field splitting parameters are greater for these sequences than for $3d$. The result is that spin pairing occurs more frequently for the later elements.

In the above discussion it was assumed that the geometric arrangement of ligands about the central atom is and remains octahedral. Under certain circumstances such is only approximately the case. Distortions, the magnitudes of which are difficult to predict, may occur in accordance with the Jahn-Teller principle. This theorem states that if an electronic state is degenerate in a given symmetry then distortion will occur so as to remove degeneracy. The resulting additional splitting will introduce additional possibilities for spectral transitions and may even alter significantly the magnetic properties. An example where the Jahn-Teller effect produces significant consequences is Cu^{++}. This is a d^9 configuration and, as indicated in Figure 2-11, a pure octahedral field produces only two levels, the transition between which would lead to a single optical absorption line.

The fact is that more than one transition is observed. The implication is that additional energy levels have appeared. From Figure 2-11 it is noted that the ground state is E, which means that it is two-fold degenerate. This corresponds to having the electron vacancy in either the $d_{x^2-y^2}$ or d_{z^2} orbital. Although these two orbitals are equal in energy for octahedral symmetry, Jahn-Teller distortion occurs to remove this degeneracy. One possible distortion is to have the two ligands on the z axis move outward, thus reducing repulsion with the d_{z^2} orbital. The electron hole would then be more favorably placed if it were in the $d_{x^2-y^2}$ orbital. Figure 2-14 represents the relative splitting of the states for a d^9 configuration when the ligand field changes

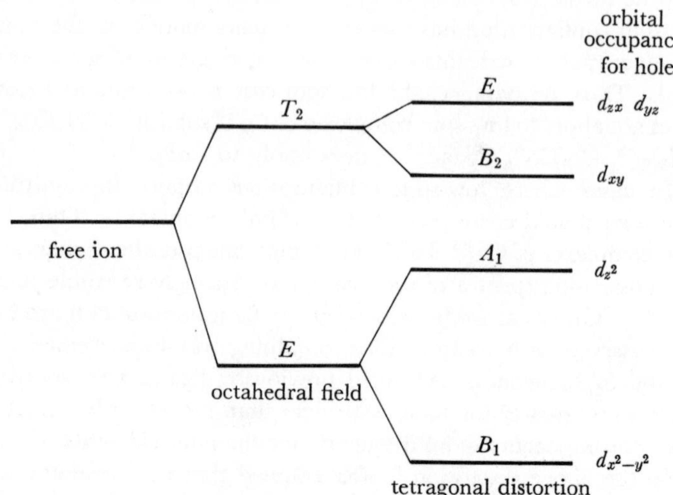

Figure 2-14 *Splitting diagram for d^9 showing Jahn-Teller effect.*

from octahedral to tetragonal by an elongation along the z axis of the octahedron. The orbital designations on the right of the diagram indicate the placing of the hole.

Other symmetries of ligand disposition sometimes encountered

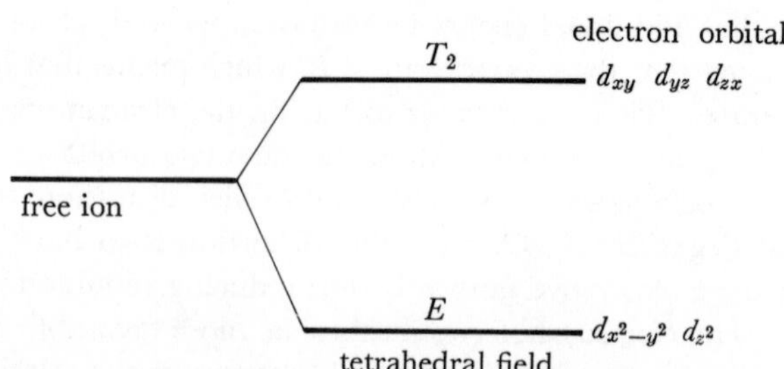

Figure 2-15 *Splitting diagram for d^1 in a tetrahedral field.*

are the tetrahedral and the square planar. Interactions between ligands and orbitals can be pictured by placing the metal atom at the center of a cube which has its edges parallel to the coordinate axes. For the tetrahedral case, four ligands are placed at alternate corners of the cube. The effect on the orbitals is the inverse of that represented in Figure 2-10—that is, the orbitals directed toward the face centers of the cube (d_{z^2}, $d_{x^2-y^2}$) interact less with the ligands than the orbitals directed toward the edges (d_{xy}, d_{yz}, d_{zx}). Thus, the e_g set of orbitals is lowered and the t_{2g} set is raised, as shown in Figure 2-15. This diagram applies to a d^1 configuration, but it could be used (with the restrictions noted above for the octahedral case) as an orbital-filling diagram for several-electron problems. Figure 2-16 is a corresponding diagram for a square-planar arrangement of ligands disposed on the x and y coordinate axes. Of the orbitals in the xy plane, the $d_{x^2-y^2}$ is more strongly affected than the d_{xy}. The orbitals not in the xy plane are less strongly affected, but their relative placing depends on the electron density distribution chosen for the ligands.

• 2-9 Molecular Parameters

In characterizing a molecular species, there are several of its features that need to be described. These include the spatial arrangement of the atomic cores, the electronic charge distribution, and the susceptibility of each of these to deformation. To compare molecular species

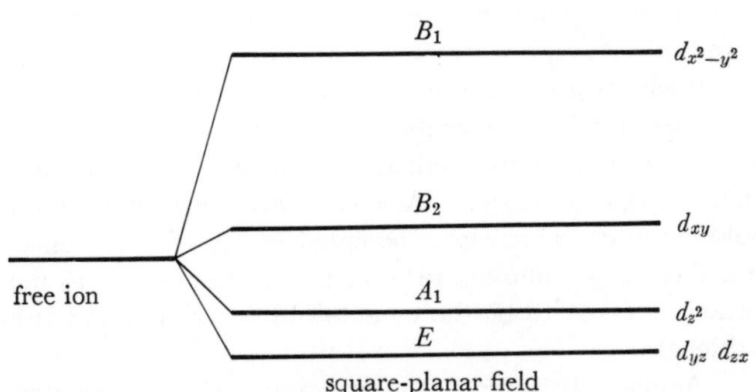

Figure 2-16 *Splitting diagram for d^1 in a square-planar field.*

with respect to these features it is necessary to have experimentally determinable parameters which can be quantitatively evaluated.

Of the fundamental parameters the most obvious is the molecular configuration in terms of interatomic distances and bond angles. These can be deduced from diffraction methods, as with X rays, neutrons, or electrons, or from spectroscopic methods, particularly those involving molecular vibrations or rotations. The diffraction methods, which depend on in-phase reinforcement of radiation, determine fixed distances between atoms. From these distances it is possible to derive interatomic distances and also angles between them.

Molecular spectroscopy methods, which depend on resonance interaction of radiation with modes of molecular motion, although less direct than diffraction methods, sometimes give more precise information. From the features of the infrared and Raman spectra, the molecular symmetry can sometimes be found. From the symmetry, the bond angles are often obvious. However, additional information is needed to determine the bond distances. This can, in favorable cases, be obtained with extreme precision from rotational transitions which depend on molecular moments of inertia, since these latter are a function of bond distances. It might be noted that the rotational spectra found in the microwave region (0.1 to 10 cm^{-1}), or as fine structure in the infrared, are related to the moments of inertia, whereas the vibrational spectra found in the infrared are related to the force constants. The *force constants* are defined as the restoring force per unit distance of bond distortion and hence give information on the deformability of the structure.

The equilibrium internuclear distance of two bonded atoms and the force opposing bond distortion can be represented graphically by means of a potential curve such as the Morse curve, shown in Figure 2-17. It represents the potential energy characteristic of a two-atom system as a function of the distance between their centers. Infinite separation is taken as the reference zero of potential energy. As the atoms are brought together, they attract each other and the potential energy decreases. At very close distances, interelectronic repulsion causes an increase of potential energy with shortened distance. Thus, there is a minimum in the curve corresponding to the distance l_e, which is taken to be the equilibrium separation and is called the bond length.

Actually, because of the uncertainty principle the atoms are not localized at this bond distance but are in vibration about it even in the lowest vibrational state ($v = 0$). The horizontal line of each vibra-

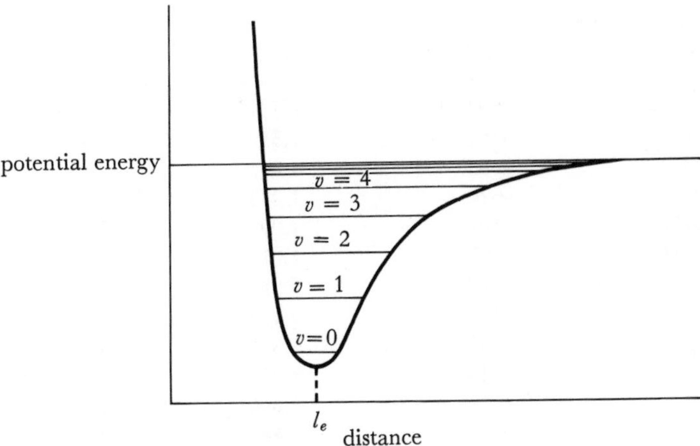

Figure 2-17 *Morse curve.*

tional quantum state implies that the potential energy is the same at both limits of the oscillation. In general, the approximation is made that the bottom of the potential well is parabolic $[V \propto (l - l_e)^2]$—that is, the slope of the curve is proportional to the displacement from the equilibrium distance l_e. The slope of the curve, derivative of energy with respect to distance, gives the force. For the parabolic approximation, force per unit distance (the second derivative of the curve) is constant and is called the force constant, k.

For systems containing more than two atoms it may be convenient to replace the distance coordinate of the Morse curve by a more general coordinate, which could for example represent an angle.

Another feature of major interest in the Morse curve of Figure 2-17 is the energy difference between the $v = 0$ state and the completely dissociated state. This energy is called the *bond dissociation energy* and is generally represented as D_0. D_0 can be determined either from spectroscopic measurements or from heats of dissociation. In the latter case, correction needs to be made for population of states above $v = 0$, $P\,\Delta V$ work, etc. Table 2-3 summarizes some typical data.

Although precise physical significance can be associated with the idea of internuclear distance, the notion of fixed *atomic radii* is considerably less tenable. The assumption that an atom is bounded independent of its environment is incorrect and, in fact, the very concept

Table 2-3 *Bond properties*[a]

Bond	D_0, kcal/mole	l_e, A	k, dyne/cm × 10^5
H—H	103.24	0.7417	5.135
Li—H	∽58	1.595	0.959
Be—H	∽53	1.343	2.109
B—H	∽70	1.233	2.80
CH_3—H	101	1.09	5.0
NH_2—H	102	1.01	6.4
HO—H	117.5	0.958	7.7
H—F	134	0.917	8.8
Na—H	47	1.887	0.73
Mg—H	46	1.731	1.17
Al—H	67	1.646	1.51
SiH_4[b]	∽75	1.48	2.77
PH_3[b]	∽76	1.42	3.2
HS—H	90?	1.33	4.0
H—Cl	102.2	1.275	4.806
H—Br	86.5	1.414	3.840
H—I	70.5	1.604	2.929
O—O	117.96	1.207	11.409
HO—OH	51	1.48	3.83
C—O	255.8	1.128	18.55
OC—O	127	1.162	15.5
N—O	162	1.151	15.5
ON—O	72	1.20	9.13
SO_2[b]	∽119	1.43	9.97
SO_3[b]	∽104	1.43	10
Li—Li	25	2.672	0.248
B—B	69?	1.589	3.457
C—C	150	1.312	9.25
N—N	225	1.094	22.40
O—O	117.96	1.207	11.409
F—F	36	1.43	4.45
Cl—Cl	57.07	1.988	3.194
Br—Br	45.46	2.284	2.425
I—I	35.55	2.666	1.701

[a] Based on values given by T. L. Cottrell, "The Strength of Chemical Bonds," 2nd ed., Butterworths, London, 1958.

[b] The given bond energy is the average of all those in the molecule listed.

of atoms in molecules is at best an approximation. Still, it is helpful to have at least some estimate of apparent sizes. It must be borne in mind that the chosen values depend on the nature of the environment—viz., bond order, coordination number, and identity of coordinated atom. **(1)** The effect of increasing bond order is to decrease the apparent size as measured by taking half of the internuclear separation. For example, in the series $H_2N—NH_2$, FN=NF, N≡N the nitrogen-nitrogen distance is 1.46, 1.25, and 1.09 A, respectively. **(2)** The effect of coordination number is difficult to determine (because of scarcity of data for cases differing only in coordination number); it may be quite large, but, in general, it is assumed to be small. **(3)** The most drastic change of all results from change of coordinated atoms. For example, as the atom in question is coordinated to atoms of increasing electronegativity, the central atom apparently decreases in size. However, this raises the question as to the division of an internuclear distance into two radii when the two bonded atoms are unlike.

The principal assumption underlying assignments of *ionic radii* is that a single characteristic radius can be designated for an ion such that it can be added to the radius of any other ion to give the observed internuclear spacing. Several methods have been used to apportion the measured spacing between the two adjacent ions. Perhaps the simplest and most straightforward procedure is that of Lande, which assumes that in crystals such as LiI the anions are so much larger than the cations that the dimensions of the lattice are fixed by "anion-anion" contact. LiI has the rock-salt structure, so that a face diagonal of the unit cell has a length equal to four times the iodide radius. Since the measured unit-cell edge length is 6.05 A, the apparent I^- radius is $(6.05\sqrt{2})/4$, or 2.14 A.

An alternate procedure, used by Pauling, introduces the assumption that the sizes of isoelectronic ions are inversely proportional to their effective atomic numbers, the latter having been calculated using screening constants. As an example, the internuclear spacing in KCl is observed to be 3.14 A. From Slater's rules (Section 1-2), the effective atomic number of K^+ is 7.40; that of Cl^-, 5.40. Thus the radius of K^+ would seem to be $5.40/(5.40 + 7.40)$ of 3.14 A, or 1.33 A. By difference, Cl^- turns out to be 1.81 A. Extending this procedure to NaF, RbBr, and CsI, Pauling obtains the radii Na^+, 0.95; F^-, 1.36; Rb^+, 1.48; Br^-, 1.95; Cs^+, 1.69; and I^-, 2.16.

Tables of ionic radii compiled by various authors generally differ slightly. Thus it is important to use all values from a single, self-

***Table 2-4** Apparent radii of atoms (in A)*

Ac^{3+}	1.18	Cu^{+}	0.96	Mg°	1.36	Pu^{4+}	0.93
Ag°	1.34	Cu^{++}	0.72	Mg^{++}	0.66		
Ag^{+}	1.26			Mn°	1.17	Ra^{++}	1.43
Ag^{++}	0.89	Dy°	1.60	Mn^{++}	0.80	Rb°	2.16
Al°	1.25	Dy^{3+}	0.92	Mn^{3+}	0.66	Rb^{+}	1.47
Al^{3+}	0.51			Mn^{4+}	0.60	Re°	1.28
Am^{3+}	1.07	Er°	1.58	Mn^{7+}	0.46	Re^{4+}	ca. 0.7
Am^{4+}	0.92	Er^{3+}	0.89	Mo°	1.30	Re^{7+}	0.56
As°	1.21	Eu°	1.85	Mo^{4+}	0.70	Rh°	1.25
As^{3+}	0.58	Eu^{3+}	0.98	Mo^{6+}	0.62	Rh^{3+}	0.68
As^{5+}	0.46					Ru°	1.25
Au°	1.34	F°	0.64	N°	0.70	Ru^{4+}	0.67
Au^{+}	1.37	F^{-}	1.33	N^{3+}	0.16		
Au^{3+}	ca. 0.9	Fe°	1.17	N^{5+}	0.13	S°	1.04
		Fe^{++}	0.74	Na°	1.57	$S^{=}$	1.84
B°	0.81	Fe^{3+}	0.64	Na^{+}	0.97	S^{4+}	0.37
B^{3+}	0.23			Nb°	1.34	S^{6+}	0.30
Ba°	1.98	Ga°	1.25	Nb^{4+}	0.74	Sb°	1.41
Ba^{++}	1.34	Ga^{3+}	0.62	Nb^{5+}	0.69	Sb^{3+}	0.76
Be°	0.89	Gd°	1.62	Nd^{3+}	1.04	Sb^{5+}	0.62
Be^{++}	0.35	Gd^{3+}	0.97	Ni°	1.15	Sc°	1.44
Bi°	ca. 1.5	Ge°	1.22	Ni^{++}	0.69	Sc^{3+}	0.81
Bi^{3+}	0.96	Ge^{++}	0.73	Np^{3+}	1.10	Se°	1.17
Bi^{5+}	0.74	Ge^{4+}	0.53	Np^{4+}	0.95	$Se^{=}$	1.98
Br°	1.14					Se^{4+}	0.50
Br^{-}	1.96	Hf°	1.44	O^{2-}	1.40	Se^{6+}	0.42
Br^{5+}	0.47	Hf^{4+}	0.78	O°	0.66	Si°	1.17
		Hg°	1.44	Os°	1.26	Si^{4+}	0.42
C°	0.77	Hg^{++}	1.10	Os^{4+}	0.69	Sm°	1.62
C^{4+}	0.16	Ho°	1.58			Sm^{3+}	1.00
Ca°	1.74	Ho^{3+}	0.91	P°	1.10	Sn°	1.40
Ca^{++}	0.99			P^{3+}	0.44	Sn^{++}	0.93
Cd°	1.41	I°	1.33	P^{5+}	0.35	Sn^{4+}	0.71
Cd^{++}	0.97	I^{-}	2.20	Pa^{4+}	0.98	Sr°	1.91
Ce°	1.65	I^{5+}	0.62	Pb°	1.54	Sr^{++}	1.12
Ce^{3+}	1.07	I^{7+}	0.50	Pb^{++}	1.20		
Ce^{4+}	0.94	In°	1.50	Pb^{4+}	0.84	Ta°	1.34
Cl°	0.99	In^{3+}	0.81	Pd°	1.28	Ta^{5+}	0.68
Cl^{-}	1.81	Ir°	1.27	Pd^{++}	0.80	Tb°	1.61
Cl^{5+}	0.34	Ir^{4+}	0.68	Pd^{4+}	0.65	Tb^{3+}	0.93
Cl^{7+}	0.27			Pm°	1.63	Tb^{4+}	0.81
Co°	1.16	K°	2.03	Pm^{3+}	1.06	Tc°	1.27
Co^{++}	0.72	K^{+}	1.33	Po°	1.53	Tc^{7+}	0.56
Co^{3+}	0.63			Pr°	1.64	Te°	1.37
Cr°	1.18	La°	1.69	Pr^{3+}	1.06	$Te^{=}$	2.21
Cr^{3+}	0.63	La^{3+}	1.14	Pr^{4+}	0.92	Te^{4+}	ca. 0.7
Cr^{6+}	0.52	Li°	1.23	Pt°	1.30	Te^{6+}	0.56
Cs°	2.35	Li^{+}	0.68	Pt^{++}	0.80	Th°	1.65
Cs^{+}	1.67	Lu°	1.56	Pt^{4+}	0.65	Th^{4+}	1.02
Cu°	1.17	Lu^{3+}	0.85	Pu^{3+}	1.08	Ti°	1.32

Table 2-4 (continued)

Ti^{3+}	0.76	U°	1.42	V^{5+}	0.59	Zn°	1.25
Ti^{4+}	0.68	U^{4+}	0.97			Zn^{++}	0.74
Tl°	1.55	U^{6+}	0.80	W°	1.30	Zr°	1.45
Tl^{+}	1.47			W^{4+}	0.70	Zr^{4+}	0.79
Tl^{3+}	0.95	V°	1.22	W^{6+}	0.62		
Tm°	1.58	V^{++}	0.88				
Tm^{3+}	0.87	V^{3+}	0.74	Y°	1.62		
		V^{4+}	0.63	Y^{3+}	0.92		

consistent set. One of the most complete sets of values is that compiled by L. H. Ahrens [*Geochim. et Cosmochim. Acta*, **2**, 155 (1952)]. Values for charged species quoted in Table 2-4 are for coordination number six and are due to Ahrens. Included in the table also are values for so-called *covalent radii* after Pauling, which are approximate sizes of the atoms when bonded to other identical atoms by single bonds. The covalent radii are those designated by superscript zero on the symbol of the element.

Data from the table must be used with caution when applied to computations involving specific compounds. For example, in the case of the perovskites (Section 3-3) S. Geller has suggested that the following radii be used: Al^{+3}, 0.56; Co^{+3}, 0.56; Cr^{+3}, 0.61; Fe^{+3}, 0.63; Ga^{+3}, 0.61; In^{+3}, 0.71; Mn^{+3}, 0.63; $O^{=}$, 1.35; Sc^{+3}, 0.69; Ti^{+3}, 0.63; V^{+3}, 0.63; and Y^{+3}, 0.77.

Thus far, most of our discussion of molecular parameters has been concerned with the arrangement of atomic nuclei and the displacement of the cores from equilibrium positions. Now we need to consider the electronic analogue—namely, the dipolar character of charge distribution and its susceptibility to deformation. When an electric field E is imposed on a sample, the effective field in the material is equal to $E + 4\pi P$, where P is the polarization of the sample. The dielectric constant is defined as the ratio of the effective field to the imposed field, or $1 + 4\pi(P/E)$. The polarization per mole, P_M, generally has a temperature-independent term and a temperature-dependent term, as follows:

$$P_M = \frac{4\pi}{3}\left(N\alpha + \frac{N\mu^2}{3kT}\right)$$

In this equation N is the Avogadro number, α is the *electric polarizability* of the molecule, and μ is the permanent electric moment of the molecule. α can be thought of as an induced moment arising from deformation of the electron charge cloud. Its units are volume and of the order of 10^{-24} cc per atom. Typical values taken from Pauling [*Proc. Roy. Soc.* (*London*), **A114,** 181 (1927)] are given in Table 2-5. Polarizability values are used in calculating short-range interactions between atoms and ions as, for example, in van der Waals attraction.

The temperature-dependent term in the polarization equation gives the *dipole moment* of the molecule. A dipole moment has the dimensions of charge times distance and is usually expressed in units of 10^{-18} esu per cm, or Debye units (D). A dipole consisting of a positive and a negative electronic charge separated by 1 angstrom has a dipole moment of 4.8D. The moments characteristic of various molecules are given in Table 2-6 (see C. P. Smyth, "Dielectric Behavior and Structure," McGraw-Hill, New York, 1955). The numbers should be considered approximate since various measurements frequently disagree by 10 per cent or more. The largest value in the table, 10.6D for KCl, might be compared to the value 12.8D, calculable from the product of the internuclear distance in KCl vapor, 2.67 A, and the unit electronic charge.

For molecules having more than two atoms, the observed moment for the molecule can be resolved into individual bond moments

Table 2-5 *Electronic polarizabilities (in 10^{-24} cc/atom)*

		H^-	He	Li^+	Be^{++}	B^{+3}	C^{+4}
		10.0	0.20	0.03	0.01	0.003	0.001
N^{-3}	$O^{=}$	F^-	Ne	Na^+	Mg^{++}	Al^{+3}	Si^{+4}
28.5	3.88	1.04	0.39	0.18	0.09	0.05	0.02
P^{-3}	$S^{=}$	Cl^-	Ar	K^+	Ca^{++}	Sc^{+3}	Ti^{+4}
41.2	10.2	3.66	1.62	0.83	0.47	0.29	0.19
As^{-3}	$Se^{=}$	Br^-	Kr	Rb^+	Sr^{++}	Y^{+3}	Zr^{+4}
28.5	10.5	4.77	2.46	1.40	0.86	0.55	0.37
Sb^{-3}	$Te^{=}$	I^-	Xe	Cs^+	Ba^{++}	La^{+3}	Ce^{+4}
31.6	14.0	7.10	3.99	2.42	1.55	1.04	0.73

Table 2-6 Dipole moments (in Debye units)

HF	1.94	CO	0.11
HCl	1.08	N_2O	0.16
HBr	0.78	NO_2	0.31
HI	0.38	N_2O_4	0.37
KF	7.3	H_2O	1.85
KCl	10.6	H_2S	0.94
CsF	7.9	NH_3	1.46
CsCl	10.5	PH_3	0.55

directed along the bond axes. To do this the bond angles need to be known. In the case of water, the moment 1.85D can be apportioned to two bond moments of 1.51D making an angle of 105° with each other. In the case of H_2S, the observed moment of 0.94D leads to two S—H moments of 0.68D at an angle of 92°.

The fact that the S—H bond moment is smaller than the O—H bond moment is not explainable in terms of bond length. Apparently, the charge transfer in the S—H bond is considerably less than in the O—H bond. Ignoring the role of the nonbonding electrons (which may be quite important), we might ascribe the difference to a smaller electronegativity difference between S and H than between O and H.

Electronegativity, unlike electron affinity, is not a directly observable physical quantity, and, in fact, there are several independent scales of electronegativity values. For example, Mulliken suggests that the mean of the ionization potential and the electron affinity be used as electronegativity. On the other hand, Pauling sets up a scale based on bond energies. Because few electron affinities have been measured, the Mulliken scale is not so practical as the Pauling scale, which is the one commonly quoted.

Table 2-7 displays recent values based on those given by Pauling ("Nature of the Chemical Bond," 3rd ed., Cornell University Press, Ithaca, N.Y., 1960, p. 93). The numbers are obtained as follows. The difference is calculated between the bond dissociation energy A—B and the geometric mean of the bond dissociation energies A—A and B—B.

$$\Delta' = D_{(A—B)} - [D_{(A—A)}D_{(B—B)}]^{1/2}$$

Table 2-7 *Electronegativities*

H																
2.1																
Li	Be											B	C	N	O	F
1.0	1.5											2.0	2.5	3.0	3.5	4.0
Na	Mg											Al	Si	P	S	Cl
0.9	1.2											1.5	1.8	2.1	2.5	3.0
K	Ca	Sc	Ti	V	Cr	Mn	Fe	Co	Ni	Cu	Zn	Ga	Ge	As	Se	Br
0.8	1.0	1.3	1.5	1.6	1.6	1.5	1.8	1.8	1.8	1.9	1.6	1.6	1.8	2.0	2.4	2.8
Rb	Sr	Y	Zr	Nb	Mo	Tc	Ru	Rh	Pd	Ag	Cd	In	Sn	Sb	Te	I
0.8	1.0	1.2	1.4	1.6	1.8	1.9	2.2	2.2	2.2	1.9	1.7	1.7	1.8	1.9	2.1	2.5
Cs	Ba	La–Lu	Hf	Ta	W	Re	Os	Ir	Pt	Au	Hg	Tl	Pb	Bi	Po	At
0.7	0.9	1.1–1.2	1.3	1.5	1.7	1.9	2.2	2.2	2.2	2.4	1.9	1.8	1.8	1.9	2.0	2.2
Fr	Ra	Ac	Th	Pa	U	Np–Lw										
0.7	0.9	1.1	1.3	1.5	1.7	1.3										

Pauling reasons that this difference Δ' is greater the greater the deviation of the bond A—B from nonpolar covalent. He assumes that any ionic character contributes additional binding energy Δ' which can be used as a measure of the electronegativity difference. In this sense electronegativity represents the tendency of an atom in a molecule to attract electrons to itself. The path from Δ' to electronegativity is substantially empirical. Because values of Δ' cannot be resolved into a linear combination of atomic parameters, the square roots of Δ' are used instead, according to the following equation:

$$x_A - x_B = 0.18\sqrt{\Delta'} + \alpha$$

x represents the electronegativity and α is an arbitrary constant which is near zero for elements other than C, N, O, and F. The value of α and the factor 0.18 are chosen in order to give a consistent set of values ranging up to 4.0 for fluorine. Clearly any scale of electronegativity must be used only in a qualitative sense.

• Supplementary Reading

In addition to other monographs of this series, the following references should prove helpful:

1. W. Kauzman, "Quantum Chemistry," Academic Press, New York, 1957.
2. C. A. Coulson, "Valence," 2nd ed., Oxford University Press, New York, 1961.
3. C. J. Ballhausen, "Introduction to Ligand Field Theory," McGraw-Hill, New York, 1962.
4. C. K. Jørgensen, "Absorption Spectra and Chemical Bonding in Complexes," Pergamon Press, London, 1962.
5. L. Pauling, "Nature of the Chemical Bond," 3rd ed., Cornell University Press, Ithaca, N.Y., 1960.
6. E. Cartmell and G. W. A. Fowles, "Valency and Molecular Structure," Butterworths, London, 1956.
7. L. E. Orgel, "Introduction to Transition-Metal Chemistry; Ligand Field Theory," Methuen, London, 1959.

3

Solid State

The preceding discussion has concerned isolated atoms and molecules, so that special interactions of the type present in condensed phases have been ignored. In this and the succeeding chapters we shall consider the problems of describing the inorganic chemistry of condensed phases. The solid state is the simpler of the condensed phases to characterize because of the long-range order that is almost invariably present. The assumption of perfect order is only an approximation even in a single crystal because of the presence of defects such as site vacancies, interstitial atoms, and dislocations of structural units. So-called "glasses," which have *no* long-range order, will not be dealt with in this book.

• 3-1 Classification

Solids can be classified on the basis of the presumed bond type (i.e., ionic, covalent, metallic, van der Waals) as well as on the basis of the crystal symmetries in terms of the interrelation of lengths and angles of the crystal axes (i.e., cubic, tetragonal, orthorhombic, hexagonal, rhombohedral, monoclinic, triclinic). Classification of crystals by bond type is based on observation of properties such as electrical conductivity, hardness, melting point, etc., in combination with chemical knowledge of the atoms involved. Classification of crystals by symmetry depends upon examination of the crystals by light reflection to determine interfacial angles or by X-ray diffraction to disclose the internal ordering.

To describe the symmetry properties of crystals, it is convenient to introduce the concept of crystallographic axes. These axes usually correspond to important directions in the crystal as defined by the faces. Three axes are sufficient to describe the crystal class and these are usually designated *a*, *b*, and *c*. In most cases the *c* axis is oriented parallel to what appears to be a unique direction of the crystal, as, for example, the direction of an elongation or compression. The *a* and *b* axes, both of which cannot be coplanar with *c*, represent other preferred directions of the crystal. Crystal planes, typical of the substance, are described according to their intersections with the axes *a*, *b*, and *c*.

The orientation of any plane can be specified by giving the relative distance from the origin of the intersection of the plane with each of the three axes. This distance is conveniently given in terms of unit cell lengths. *Miller indices* are numbers which are obtained from the reciprocals of these intersection distances. In case a plane is parallel to one of the axes, it intersects only at infinity and its Miller index is zero. Figure 3-1 gives the Miller indices for three faces of a cube. In this particular case, the three axes *a*, *b*, and *c* are equivalent, so that all the faces are equivalent and can be represented by one set of Miller indices, usually given as $\{100\}$.

The seven crystal classes differ from each other in the angles included between the three axes and in the magnitude of the repeat distances *a*, *b*, and *c*. Table 3-1 classifies the systems in terms of *a*, *b*, and *c* and α, β, and γ, the latter being the angles between the axes. Because it is conceivable that within the resolving power of X rays nearly equal distances or angles may appear identical, crystal classification is more rigorously made in terms of structural symmetry. The last column of Table 3-1 gives the essential symmetry elements that distinguish each class of crystals. (The complete set of symmetry operations describing a particular figure is called the "point group" of that

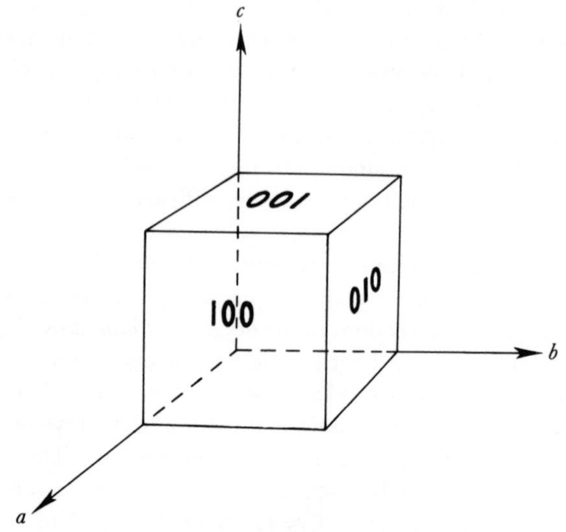

Figure 3-1 Miller indices of a cube.

figure.) An n-fold axis is a symmetry operation which corresponds to rotation of a figure producing indistinguishable configurations n times in one complete revolution.

From the external symmetry of a well-developed crystal, it is sometimes possible to make inferences as to the internal ordering of the atomic planes. However, it is usually necessary to get this information from X-ray analysis. In X-ray analysis, an X-ray beam of monochromatic radiation is allowed to impinge on the sample, either powder or single crystal, placed at the center of a cylindrical film or other detector. The angles through which the incident beam is diffracted are the prime data, since by use of the Bragg relation,

$$\lambda = 2d \sin \theta$$

each angle of deviation, 2θ (= angle of incidence plus angle of reflection), is related to a characteristic interplanar spacing, d, depending on the wavelength of the X rays used, λ. The relation between the

Table 3-1 *Crystal classes*

Class	Unit-cell condition	Symmetry
Cubic	$a = b = c$ $\alpha = \beta = \gamma = 90°$	Four threefold axes
Tetragonal	$a = b \neq c$ $\alpha = \beta = \gamma = 90°$	One fourfold axis
Orthorhombic	$a \neq b \neq c$ $\alpha = \beta = \gamma = 90°$	Three mutually perpendicular twofold axes or two reflection planes intersecting in a twofold axis
Hexagonal	$a = b \neq c$ $\alpha = \beta = 90°$; $\gamma = 120°$	One sixfold axis
Rhombohedral	$a = b = c$ $\alpha = \beta = \gamma \neq 90°$	One threefold axis
Monoclinic	$a \neq b \neq c$ $\alpha = \beta = 90° \neq \gamma$	One twofold axis and a plane of symmetry perpendicular to it or one reflection plane
Triclinic	$a \neq b \neq c$ $\alpha \neq \beta \neq \gamma$	None

various values of d observed with a particular substance is fixed by the symmetry of the atomic arrangement in the crystals.

For example, a simple cubic structure gives a powder pattern consisting of a series of regularly spaced lines with the seventh, fifteenth, and twenty-third lines missing. The reason for the missing lines is that the only possible interplanar spacings for simple cubic are those given by the geometrical relation

$$d = a(h^2 + k^2 + l^2)^{-1/2}$$

where a is the unit-cell length and h, k, and l are Miller indices. The numbers 7, 15, 23, etc., are not sums of squares of integers. For face-centered cubic and body-centered cubic, the conditions for extinction of lines are different from those for simple cubic. For structures of lower symmetry the analysis becomes more complicated and for complete determination of atomic positions it is necessary to study diffraction from a single crystal, particularly as to the intensity of the diffracted radiation as a function of the orientation of the crystal relative to the incident beam.

The atomic arrangement in a given crystal structure can be described in terms of an infinite collection of points, called the *space lattice*. This distribution in space can be generated by repeated translation of a unit cell along its characteristic axes. There are but 14 different unit cells possible, corresponding to the 14 Bravais translational lattices. These are: for the cubic system—simple, body-centered, and face-centered; for the tetragonal system—simple and body-centered; for the orthorhombic—simple, base-centered, body-centered, and face-centered; for the monoclinic—simple and base-centered; for the hexagonal, rhombohedral, and triclinic—just one each. These translational lattices do not specify the local symmetry about each given point. For example, $CO_3^{=}$ has one threefold and three twofold rotation axes. In the hexagonal form of $CaCO_3$, the structure symmetry must be consistent with this carbonate ion symmetry as well as the symmetry of the Bravais lattice. Complete specification of a crystal structure requires designation of its *space group*, which includes the translational symmetry as well as the point group symmetry. There are 230 space groups possible, based on 14 Bravais lattices and 32 point groups.

• 3-2 Ionic Crystals

The simplest representatives of ionic solids are the alkali halides. Except for CsCl, CsBr, CsI (which have simple cubic configurations with each ion surrounded cubically by eight neighbors of opposite sign), the alkali halides have the rock-salt structure. The rock-salt structure can be envisioned as two interpenetrating face-centered cubic arrangements—one consisting only of cations, the other of anions. In the rock-salt structure, each ion is surrounded octahedrally by six ions of opposite charge.

From the arrangement of ions it is possible to calculate the *crystal energy* or *lattice energy*—i.e., the energy necessary to separate the ions to infinite distance. The details of the calculation depend on the following considerations. The equilibrium separation of a cation-anion pair is fixed by a balance of the electrostatic attraction and repulsion. For a pair the interaction energy, E_p, can be written

$$E_p = -\frac{z_1 z_2 e^2}{r} + \frac{b}{r^n}$$

where z_1 and z_2 are the ionic charge numbers, e is the electronic charge, r is the internuclear separation, and b and n are constants of repulsion to be evaluated. For a mole of salt, the lattice energy U is given by

$$U = N\left(-\frac{Az_1 z_2 e^2}{r} + \frac{B}{r^n}\right)$$

where N is the Avogadro number and A is the Madelung constant, a geometrical factor which takes into account the other ions in the crystal.

For a NaCl structure the Madelung constant can be calculated as the sum of all the interaction terms between, say, a given Na^+ and all the other ions in the crystal considered to be placed on a cubic lattice at progressively greater distances from the reference ion. If a is the distance between Na^+ and the nearest Cl^-, then there are 6 Cl^- at distance a giving an attractive potential energy of $-6e^2/a$; there are 12 Na^+ at distance $\sqrt{2}a$, giving a repulsive potential of $+(12/\sqrt{2}a)e^2$; there are 8 Cl^- at distance $\sqrt{3}a$, giving a repulsive potential of $-8e^2/\sqrt{3}a$; and so on. The potential energy is given by a series of the form

$$\frac{e^2}{a}\left(-\frac{6}{\sqrt{1}} + \frac{12}{\sqrt{2}} - \frac{8}{\sqrt{3}} + \cdots\right)$$

There is no obvious cutoff for the series, since large positive and large negative terms continue to alternate. That the series converges can be seen by examining progressively larger electrically neutral cubes centered on the reference ion. The neutrality condition gives a faster falloff in potential and can be achieved by taking fractional charges—

i.e., $\frac{1}{2}$ for a face ion, $\frac{1}{4}$ for an edge, and $\frac{1}{8}$ for a corner. The terms analogous to the above for a neutrality calculation would give

$$\frac{e^2}{a}\left[-\frac{6(\frac{1}{2})}{\sqrt{1}}+\frac{12(\frac{1}{4})}{\sqrt{2}}-\frac{8(\frac{1}{8})}{\sqrt{3}}+\cdots\right]$$

Consideration of only the ions in a unit cell centered on a Na^+ ion gives a value of 1.46 as a first approximation to the Madelung constant A. A better estimate can be obtained by including a second cubic shell of neighbors. Figure 3-2 can be visualized as a cross-sectional slice through the reference ion. The unit cell used for the first approximation contains the central ion and a fraction of the ions in the inner square. For the second approximation the remaining fraction of the inner-square ions and an appropriate fraction of the ions in the outer

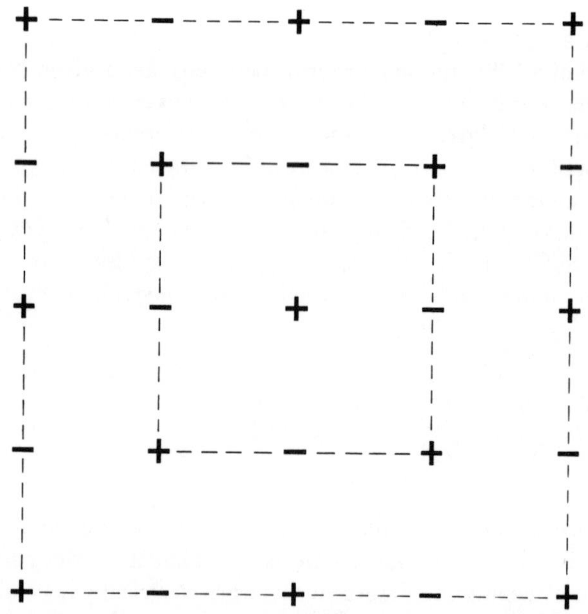

Figure 3-2 *Two-dimensional ion network of NaCl.*

square need to be considered along with the corresponding ions in the other dimension. For the second shell the contribution to the potential energy is

$$\frac{e^2}{a}\left[-\frac{6(\frac{1}{2})}{\sqrt{1}}+\frac{12(\frac{3}{4})}{\sqrt{2}}-\frac{8(\frac{7}{8})}{\sqrt{3}}+\frac{6(\frac{1}{2})}{\sqrt{4}}-\frac{24(\frac{1}{2})}{\sqrt{5}}\right.$$
$$\left.+\frac{24(\frac{1}{2})}{\sqrt{6}}+\frac{12(\frac{1}{4})}{\sqrt{8}}-\frac{24(\frac{1}{4})}{\sqrt{9}}+\frac{8(\frac{1}{8})}{\sqrt{12}}\right]$$

The first three terms count the remaining fractions of the ions of the inner shell. The fourth term comes from the six Na^+ ions face-centered on the larger cube—the fifth term, from the twenty-four chloride ions adjacent to the Na^+ on the faces. The root five enters because the distance from the reference ion is two lattice spacings over and one perpendicular. The root six term counts the 24 Na^+ ions which are typified by two steps over in the x direction followed by one in the y and another in the z. The root eight term corresponds to positive ions on the edge centers, the root nine to the adjacent negative ions along the edge, and the root twelve to the Na^+ on the corners. The total contribution by the second shell is 0.28, thus leading to a second approximation of A as 1.74. From here on convergence is rapid and the value of A for a rock-salt structure is 1.747558. For a CsCl structure, A is 1.762670.

The constant b can be evaluated by differentiating U with respect to r, setting the derivative equal to zero, and solving for b in terms of n and the equilibrium internuclear spacing a. The point of differentiation is to define the energy minimum,

$$\frac{dU}{dr} = N\left(\frac{Az_1z_2e^2}{a^2} - \frac{nB}{a^{n+1}}\right) = 0$$

from which

$$B = \frac{Az_1z_2e^2}{n}\,a^{n-1}$$

The constant n can be evaluated from the compressibility and has values of the order of 9 to 12. The final expression for the crystal energy is

$$U = N\left(-\frac{Az_1z_2e^2}{a} + \frac{Az_1z_2e^2}{na^n}a^{n-1}\right)$$

$$= -\frac{NAz_1z_2e^2}{a}\left(1 - \frac{1}{n}\right)$$

Table 3-2 presents values calculated for the crystal energies of various representative solids using a modification of the above equa-

Table 3-2 *Crystal energies of solids (in kcal/mole)* [a]

Salt	Calc.	Exp.	Salt	Calc.	Exp.
LiF	244	241	BeO	1082	
LiCl	200	198	BeS	893	
LiBr	190	189	MgO	938	
LiI	176	175	MgS	788	
NaF	215	216	CaO	841	
NaCl	184	184	CaS	726	
NaBr	176	176	SrO	792	
NaI	164	165	SrS	692	
KF	193	192	BaO	746	
KCl	168	167	BaS	659	
KBr	161	161			
KI	152	151	NaOH	197	
LiH	234	217	KOH	175	
NaH	202	194			
KH	177	171	TiO	916	928
			VO	940	936
AgF	220	228	MnO	890	911
AgCl	199	216	FeO	907	938
AgBr	195	214	CoO	917	954
AgI	186	211	NiO	934	974
			ZnO	977	964

[a] After T. C. Waddington, "Advances in Inorganic Chemistry and Radiochemistry," Vol. I, Academic Press, New York, 1959.

tion which takes into account zero-point energy and a more complex description of repulsive terms. Included for comparison are experimentally determined values which come either from direct measurement or indirectly from an energy cycle known generally as the Born-Haber cycle (I). The lattice energy, U, is calculated as the sum of the

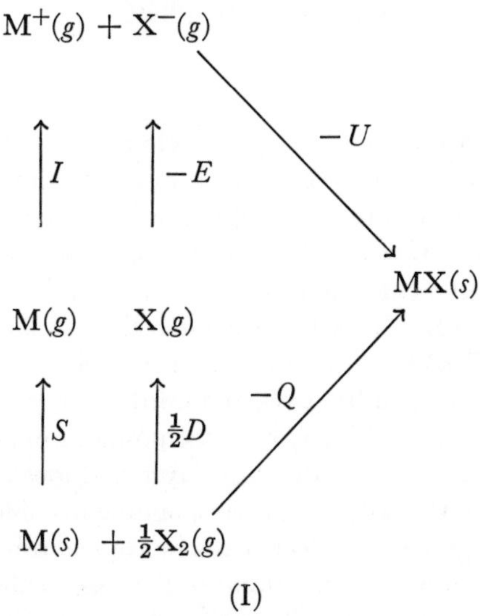

(I)

energy of formation Q, the sublimation energy S, ionization energy I, half the dissociation energy D, and the negative of the electron affinity E. For sodium chloride, Q at absolute zero is 98 kcal; S is 26 kcal; I is 118 kcal; $\frac{1}{2}D$ is 29 kcal; and $-E$ is -87 kcal. Thus, U is 184 kcal.

• 3-3 Packing of Atoms

Many of the most important structures encountered in inorganic chemistry can be related to the close-packing of spheres. There are two ways that spheres can be close-packed with the same efficiency of space utilization (74 per cent of the total volume is filled by the spheres themselves). These are called hexagonal close-packed and cubic close-packed and are designated *hcp* and *ccp*, respectively. Although *ccp* is identical with face-centered cubic, it is usually more helpful to visualize these structures in terms of relative stacking of layers.

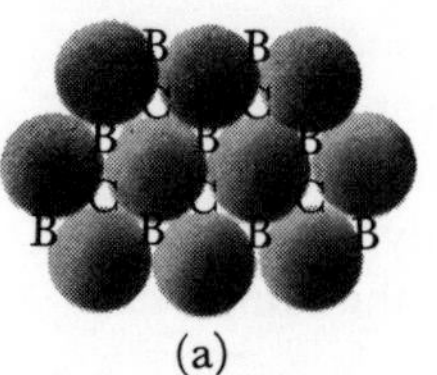

(a)

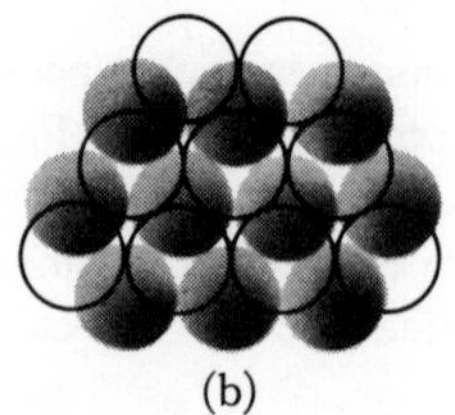
(b)

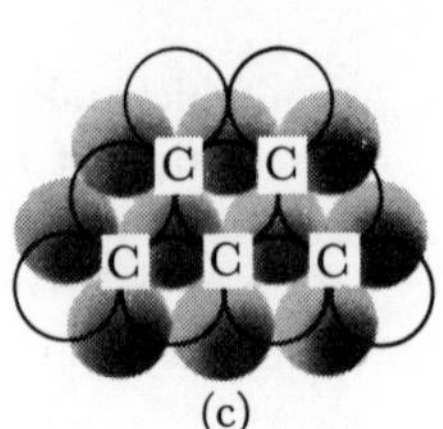

(c)

Figure 3-3 *Close-packing of spheres.*

Figure 3-3a represents a layer of close-packed spheres with interstices for the next superposed layer marked with letters. If the second layer is placed so that the spheres fit into interstices marked B, Figure 3.3b results. If now a third layer of spheres is added, two alternatives exist. In one case the third-layer spheres fit directly over the bottom-layer spheres. This is hexagonal close-packing and can be represented as ABABA . . ., where A and B refer to the two alternate layer positions. In the other case, the third layer spheres fit into the C positions—that is, not directly over the positions in either of the two lower layers. In Figure 3-3c the third-layer positions are indicated by C for the sequence ABCABC . . ., corresponding to cubic close-packing. The unit cell for *hcp* may be selected as a hexagonal prism, in which the hexagonal face consists of one atom and its six coplanar neighbors. The layer above the base contributes 3 atoms to the unit cell, and the top layer, which is identical with the base, contributes $1\frac{1}{2}$ atoms, as does the base. Thus, the number of atoms in this unit cell is 6. It might be noted that the conventional unit cell for *hcp* is one-third of the above prism and thus contains but 2 atoms. For cubic close-packed, the unit cell is usually better chosen as the face-centered-cubic cell, in which the stacking layer can be defined as passing through three nonadjacent corners of the cube. The face-centered-cubic unit cell contains 4 atoms.

Among the common materials that crystallize with nearly hexagonal close-packing are many of the metals such as magnesium, β-calcium, zinc, cadmium, yttrium, α-lanthanum, α-thallium, titanium, hafnium, and β-chromium. Also showing hexagonal close-packing is solid H_2. Face-centered cubic is represented by most of the rare gases; some simple rotating molecules, such as CH_4 and HCl; and many metals, including strontium, α-calcium, aluminum, β-lanthanum, β-thallium, lead, γ-iron, and nickel.

Consideration of the structures represented in Figure 3-3 discloses that there are two kinds of interstices between the spheres of a close-packed array. These are usually referred to as octahedral and tetrahedral holes, corresponding to six and four neighboring atoms, respectively. Referring to Figure 3-3b, we note that the holes in the top layer fall either over holes in the bottom layer or over the centers of spheres. In the former case, an octahedral hole is formed midway between the two layers. The six neighboring atoms, three from each sheet, form a regular octahedron. In the latter case, a tetrahedral hole is formed by the three atoms of the top sheet and the underlying atom of the bottom sheet. In addition, there is another tetrahedral hole under each atom of the top sheet, formed by it and the three adjacent atoms of the bottom sheet. Thus, although the number of octahedral holes equals the number of atoms per sheet, there will be twice as many tetrahedral holes as there are octahedral holes.

A large number of inorganic compounds have structures in which the atoms of one element can be considered to define a close-packed array in which other atoms are distributed in the holes. An adequate description of the structure can then be given merely by stating whether octahedral or tetrahedral holes are occupied and to what extent. For example, the *rock-salt* structure is describable as a cubic close-packed array of anions, with the cations occupying all the octahedral holes. Table 3-3 lists several specific examples. The case in which a cubic close-packed array has all its tetrahedral holes occupied is represented either by the *fluorite* or *antifluorite* structure. In the former (e.g., CaF_2), the cations can be envisioned as occupying cubic close-packed lattice sites with the anions centered on the tetrahedral holes; in the latter (e.g., Li_2O), the anions form the cubic close-packed array. Systematic occupancy of half the octahedral holes, A, in a cubic close-packed array, B, gives materials of general formula AB_2 (e.g., W_2N). Systematic occupancy of half the tetrahedral holes, A, in a cubic close-packed array, B, gives materials of general formula AB (e.g., ZnS—*zincblende*). Similarly, two-thirds occupancy of the octahedral holes gives A_2B_3, as in the *corundum* structure (e.g., α-Al_2O_3). Other examples of close-packed derivative structures are found in Table 3-3.

In a close-packed array of anions, the size of the octahedral and tetrahedral holes is different, so the size of the cation relative to the anion—the so-called radius ratio—determines which kind of holes it occupies. The easiest way to see the size of the tetrahedral hole is to

Table 3-3 Close-packed derivative structures

Holes used	Fraction filled	Name	Examples
Octahedral	1	Rock salt	Halides of Li, Na, K, Rb; CsF; NH_4Cl, NH_4Br, NH_4I, AgF, AgCl, AgBr; oxides, sulfides, selenides of Mg, Ca, Sr, Ba; TiO, VO, MnO, CdO, MnS, PbS, EuS, PuS, LiH, TiC, ZrC, ScN, TiN, CrN
Octahedral	$\frac{2}{3}$	Corundum	α-Al_2O_3, α-Fe_2O_3, Ti_2O_3, V_2O_3, Cr_2O_3, α-Ga_2O_3, Rh_2O_3
Octahedral	$\frac{1}{2}$		Mo_2N, W_2N
Octahedral	$\frac{1}{4}$		Mn_4N, Fe_4N
Tetrahedral	1	Antifluorite	Oxides, sulfides, selenides, tellurides of Li, Na, K; Rb_2O, Rb_2S
		Fluorite	CaF_2, SrF_2, $SrCl_2$, BaF_2, PbF_2, EuF_2, CeO_2, PrO_2, HfO_2, ThO_2, UO_2, NpO_2, PuO_2, AmO_2, TiH_2
Tetrahedral	$\frac{1}{2}$	Zincblende	CuCl, CuBr, CuI, AgI, BeS, BeSe, BeTe, ZnS, ZnSe, ZnTe, β-CdS, CdTe, AlP, AlAs, AlSb, GaP, GaAs, GaSb, InSb, TiH, ZrH
Tetrahedral	$\frac{1}{4}$		Pd_2H
Tetrahedral	$\frac{1}{8}$		Zr_4H

consider four spheres located at alternate corners of a cube. The hole center corresponds to the cube center. Because the anions make contact along the face diagonal, the hole radius is the difference between half the body diagonal and half the face diagonal. With anions of radius r, the hole is equal to $\frac{1}{2}(\sqrt{6}r) - \frac{1}{2}(2r)$, or $0.225r$. In an oxide lattice, where r is 1.40 A for the anion, cations smaller than 0.315 A should fit in the tetrahedral holes. For octahedral holes, the hole radius is $(\sqrt{2} - 1)r$, or $0.414r$. This could be visualized as the difference between half the diagonal and half the edge of a square outlined by four of the six coordinate neighbors. For oxides, octahedral holes can accommodate cations up to 0.580 A. Given a cation which is small enough to fit either into a tetrahedral or an octahedral hole, the tetrahedral hole is favored, since it leads to shorter anion-cation separation and hence to lower Coulomb energy.

As with ionic radii themselves these radius-ratio critical values ought to be considered approximate. For example, whereas B^{+3} ($r = 0.23$ A) easily fits into tetrahedral holes, so does Be^{+2}($r = 0.35$ A) even though the latter exceeds the critical size for tetrahedral fit. Mg^{++}($r = 0.66$ A), however, will not fit tetrahedral holes as defined by packing of hard spheres; in fact, it is not expected to fit octahedral holes either. In MgO there is expansion of the oxide lattice (oxygen-to-oxygen distance 3.15 A instead of 2.80 A) to accommodate the magnesium ions.

Compounds more complicated than the above binary examples may also be related to close-packed structures. Examples are furnished by the spinels, compounds of general formula AB_2O_4, named after the mineral spinel, $MgAl_2O_4$. In the *spinels* oxygen atoms are in cubic close-packed arrangement with the cations distributed over both the tetrahedral and octahedral sites.

Spinels are frequently classed as *normal*, if the A atoms are in tetrahedral holes and the B in octahedral, or as *inverse*, if the A atoms are in octahedral holes and the B in both. An important example of an inverse spinel is Fe_3O_4 if we consider the iron atoms to be of two oxidation states. X-ray scattering does not give unequivocal assignment of oxidation state to the atoms in the different sites. However, from conductivity and magnetic studies it is inferred that the tetrahedral sites are occupied by half of the ferric ions and the octahedral sites by ferrous ions and the remaining half of the ferric ions. Examples of spinels are given in Table 3-4. Because the same kind of atom can occur on both types of sites, it is possible to get spinels of formula other than AB_2O_4. Examples are $LiAl_5O_8$ and $Li_4Ti_5O_{12}$.

Also related to the close-packed structure is the series of compounds called *perovskites*, of formula ABX_3. They are named after the mineral perovskite, $CaTiO_3$. The perovskite structure can be considered as a single close-packed array of two kinds of atoms (in this case, Ca and O) with the third kind (Ti) systematically distributed over $\frac{1}{4}$ of the octahedral holes. In general A is the larger of the two cations A and B, since it is the one which, with the anion X, forms the close-packed array. The smaller cation, B, fills all those octahedral holes formed exclusively by the anions. As was noted previously, there

Table 3-4 Spinels

Formula	Tetrahedral hole	Octahedral hole	Class
$MgAl_2O_4$	Mg	Al	Normal
$MnAl_2O_4$	Mn	Al	Normal
$FeAl_2O_4$	Fe	Al	Normal
$CoAl_2O_4$	Co	Al	Normal
$NiAl_2O_4$	Ni	Al	Normal
$ZnAl_2O_4$	Zn	Al	Normal
$MgCr_2O_4$	Mg	Cr	Normal
$NiCr_2O_4$	Ni	Cr	Normal
$CdCr_2O_4$	Cd	Cr	Normal
$ZnFe_2O_4$	Zn	Fe	Normal
$CdFe_2O_4$	Cd	Fe	Normal
$CuFe_2O_4$	Fe	Cu, Fe	Inverse
$MgFe_2O_4$	Fe	Mg, Fe	Inverse
$MgIn_2O_4$	In	Mg, In	Inverse
$TiZn_2O_4$	Zn	Zn, Ti	Inverse
$SnZn_2O_4$	Zn	Zn, Sn	Inverse
$SnCo_2O_4$	Co	Co, Sn	Inverse
Fe_3O_4	Fe(III)	Fe(II), Fe(III)	Inverse

is one octahedral hole for each close-packed atom. In a layer composed of AX_3 units three of the four octahedral holes are necessarily adjacent to A, leaving only one position for a B atom. Figure 3-4 shows one way of representing a unit cell for the perovskite structure. The close-packing planes (defined by cross-hatching) pass through alternate corners of the cube and three adjacent face centers. In the unit cell shown, the octahedral cavity allowed for B occupancy is formed by three X atoms in each of the adjacent close-packing planes.

In general, X of the perovskites is either oxygen or a halogen. In the first case, the charge of A and B totals six; in the latter case, three. Possible combinations for ABO_3 are $+1$ with $+5$, $+2$ with $+4$, and $+3$ with $+3$. For ABX_3 (X = halogen), the only possibility is $+1$ with $+2$. Typical examples are given in Table 3-5.

Actually, the idealized cubic perovskite structure is rarely obtained. As can be seen from Figure 3-4, the cubic condition demands that the internuclear A-X distance (equal to half the length of the face diagonal) be $\sqrt{2}$ times the internuclear B-X distance (equal to half

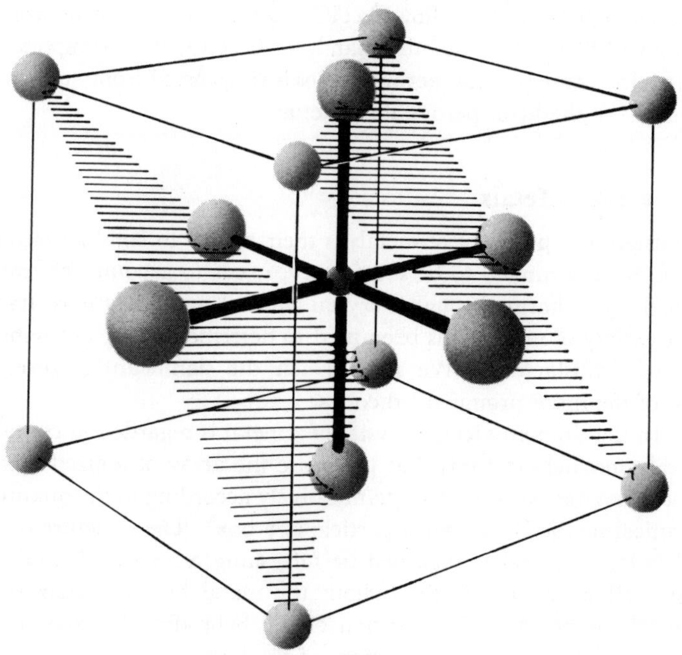

Figure 3-4 Perovskite unit cell.

the length of an edge). This requires that the sum of the radii of A and of X be equal to $\sqrt{2}$ times the sum of the radii of B and of X. For $BaTiO_3$, the sum of the Ba^{++} and $O^{=}$ radii, 2.74 A (see Table 2-4), is 1.32 times the sum of the Ti^{+4} and $O^{=}$ radii, 2.08 A. Apparently this

Table 3-5 *Perovskites*

Cation charge	
+1, +5	$NaNbO_3$, $KNbO_3$, $AgNbO_3$, $AgTaO_3$
+2, +4	$SrTiO_3$, $SrZrO_3$, $SrHfO_3$, $SrSnO_3$, $BaTiO_3$, $BaZrO_3$, $BaSnO_3$, $BaCeO_3$, $BaPrO_3$, $BaThO_3$
+3, +3	$LaAlO_3$, $LaTiO_3$, $LaCrO_3$, $LaMnO_3$, $LaFeO_3$
+1, +2	$KMgF_3$, $KNiF_3$, $KZnF_3$

is close enough to $\sqrt{2}$ to allow $BaTiO_3$ to have a cubic structure, at least above 120°C. On the other hand, for $CaTiO_3$ the corresponding ratio is 1.15; consequently, perovskite itself is distorted from cubic and does not have the ideal perovskite structure.

• 3-4 Metals

The outstanding property of metals is their ability to conduct electric current. So any model, to be satisfactory, needs to account for transport of electric charge through a crystal without significant mass transfer. A variety of models has been used to describe metals, but none is completely satisfactory. We shall sketch the significant features of several of the more prominent theories.

In the simplest view, a crystal of a metal is regarded as containing freely moving electrons that permeate the array of ionized atoms. The problem has been treated quantitatively according to the quantum mechanical methods used for a particle in a box. The structure of the metal is ignored and is regarded as furnishing a "square" potential energy well which is flat throughout the metal but rises sharply at the metal boundary. The solution of the Schrödinger equation for this potential leads to wave functions of the form

$$\psi = Ce^{-i(kr+\omega t)}$$

In these functions C is a constant, k is a wave vector pointing in the direction of wave motion and equal in magnitude to 2π times the reciprocal of the wavelength λ, r is a distance vector in the crystal, ω is 2π times the frequency ν, and t is the time.

It should be noted that these functions are time-dependent and correspond to traveling waves in the crystal. Positive and negative values of k correspond to waves traveling in opposite direction. The energy associated with any one of these waves is given by the expression

$$E = \frac{h^2k^2}{8\pi^2m}$$

where m is the mass of the electron. Figure 3-5 gives a graph of this quadratic dependence of energy on wave vector for free electrons in a one-dimensional lattice. Strictly speaking, k is quantized; however, because the crystal is usually much larger than the electron wave-

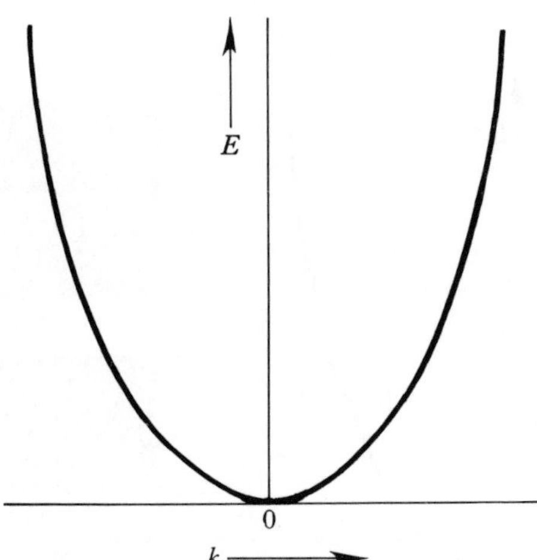

Figure 3-5 *Energy as a function of wave vector for free-electron model.*

length, a large number of states is possible, so that the curve is essentially continuous. The continuum of energy levels constitutes a band. For any of the energy states within the band there are two electrons, moving in opposite directions, so there is no net conductivity. In the presence of an electric field, electrons moving down field are accelerated—i.e., moved to higher states—and thus dominate.

The free-electron model accounts for the phenomenon of conductivity; there is a problem, however, in accounting for nonconductivity of insulators. It does no good to argue that insulators are substances in which electrons are bound to individual atoms, since electron wave functions extend over distances significantly larger than interatomic dimensions (quantum mechanical tunneling). Calculations indicate that the largest potential energy barriers—corresponding to atoms of largest ionization potential—can only account for a decrease of 10^2 in conductivity from the free-electron model. Actually, the experimental conductivities for insulators are as much as 10^{24} times as small as for metals.

The existence of insulators implies that there cannot be a continuum of energy levels as implied in Figure 3-5. Considerations of lattice periodicity lead to forbidden ranges of energy. These forbidden

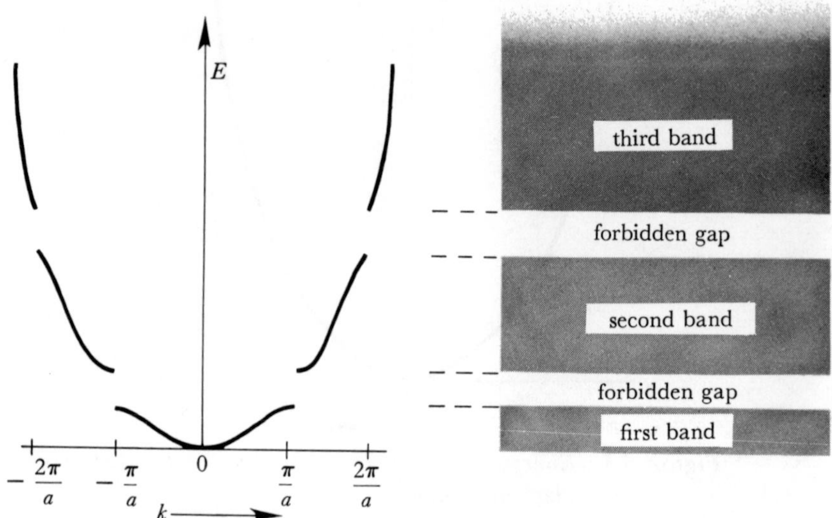

Figure 3-6 *Forbidden gaps in the energy vs. wave vector relation.*

energies can be rationalized as corresponding to those for which the electron wavelength matches the periodicity of the lattice; by the Bragg law, these electrons should be reflected and not be capable of existing in the crystal as traveling waves. Figure 3-6 shows for the one-dimensional case discontinuities in the energy function for values of the wave vector corresponding to integral multiples of the reciprocal lattice spacing, $1/a$. From the Bragg relation $n\lambda = 2a \sin \theta$ ($\theta = 90°$), diffraction occurs when $\lambda = 2a/n$. Since $k = 2\pi/\lambda$, diffraction occurs when $k = n\pi/a$. The values of the energy E corresponding to $-\pi/a < k < \pi/a$ constitute the first energy band of the particular solid. At $k = \pi/a$ and $k = -\pi/a$, there is a forbidden energy gap, as there is at each integral multiple of π/a.

The energy states that make up a band can be considered to be analogous to molecular orbitals extending over the whole crystal. Each molecular orbital is approximated as arising from the overlap of atomic wave functions from all the atoms. The total number of states belonging to a particular band is equal to the number of atoms contributing. The band width—that is, the energy difference between the highest and the lowest M.O. of the set—is independent of the number of atoms contributing; it is a function only of the spacing and the identity of the atomic functions. For example, *d* bands (derived from atomic *d* functions) are generally narrower than *p* or *s* bands of the same principal quantum number. In any case, electronic population of a band is limited to $2N$, where N is the number of atomic orbitals.

In the band picture, whether a substance is an insulator or a metal depends on the degree of filling of the levels in the band. In a completely filled band there are as many electrons moving down field as up field. Furthermore, down-field electrons cannot be accelerated because, owing to the forbidden gap, there are no readily accessible higher states. The material is an insulator. On the other hand, in a metal such as sodium the energy band is not filled, and application of an electric field can accelerate electrons by use of immediately adjacent higher states.

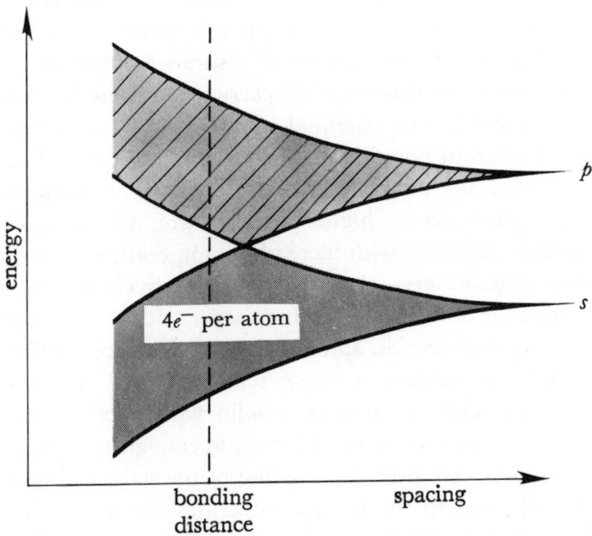

Figure 3-7 *Generation of forbidden gap due to symmetry requirements.*

Because complications may arise when bands from different atomic states overlap, it is not always easy to predict metallic properties. For example, in the case of magnesium it would appear that the 3*s* band would be completely populated, since there are two electrons for each atom. However, the 3*p* level in isolated Mg atoms is so close to the 3*s* level that on bringing the Mg atoms together the energy level broadening (band formation) gives rise to band overlap. Thus, energy levels are available to the Mg electrons and conductivity can occur. Actually, when *s* bands and *p* bands overlap, they lose their identity and the resulting levels are best described as hybrid levels.

In the case of the diamond structure (e.g., carbon, silicon, germanium, grey tin), overlap of *s* and *p* bands does not result in any partially filled bands, as would be necessary for conduction. Owing to the symmetry of the atomic alignment there is imposed a forbidden gap in the overlapped region (Figure 3-7). At the actual bonding distance, four electrons per atom just fill all the levels below the forbidden gap.

• 3-5 Semiconductors

Classification of solids as metals or semiconductors is not only a matter of the lesser conductivity of the latter but also, more fundamentally, of an opposite temperature coefficient of resistance. Metals owe their electrical resistance to scattering of carrier electrons by interaction with a nonperiodic lattice potential as introduced by lattice defects (e.g., impurities, grain boundaries, vacant sites) or thermal motion of the lattice. Since the carrier concentration stays constant while the lattice motion increases at higher temperature, the conductivity of metals generally decreases with increasing temperature. On the other hand, semiconductors are substances with relatively few conducting electrons; when the number of these increases rapidly with temperature, the conductivity increases in spite of increased lattice motion.

Perhaps the simplest type of semiconductor is the so-called "intrinsic" semiconductor—that is, a solid with filled valence bands but for which the conduction band lies close enough to it that thermal excitation can populate it at the expense of the valence band. If we designate by E_g the gap energy that separates the top of the valence from the bottom of the conduction band, then n, the number of carriers per cubic centimeter in the conduction band, is given by

$$n = \text{constant } e^{-E_g/2kT}$$

The equation can be derived by considering the excitation process to be a chemical reaction in which an electron pair bond is broken so as to yield a free-moving charge in the conduction band and a vancancy ("hole") in the valence band accessible for electron motion. Writing the reaction as

$$e \text{ in valence band} \rightleftharpoons e \text{ in conduction band} + \text{hole in valence band}$$

and designating the concentration of products as n and p, respectively, we can write

$$n = p = K^{1/2} = e^{\Delta S/2R}e^{-\Delta H/2RT} = Ce^{-E_g/2kT}$$

K is an equilibrium constant; ΔS and ΔH are the entropy and the enthalpy of the activation process.

In this derivation we have used the assumption that the density of electrons in the valence band is constant. This is reasonable since the total number of electrons in the valence band is very large compared to the number excited. The equality $n = p$ is valid only so long as there are no impurity atoms which can donate electrons to the conduction band and no impurity atoms which can accept or trap electrons from the valence band. Even though $n = p$, conduction may be predominantly by one type of carrier if the mobility of the other carrier is so small as to lead to a negligible conductivity contribution. In the

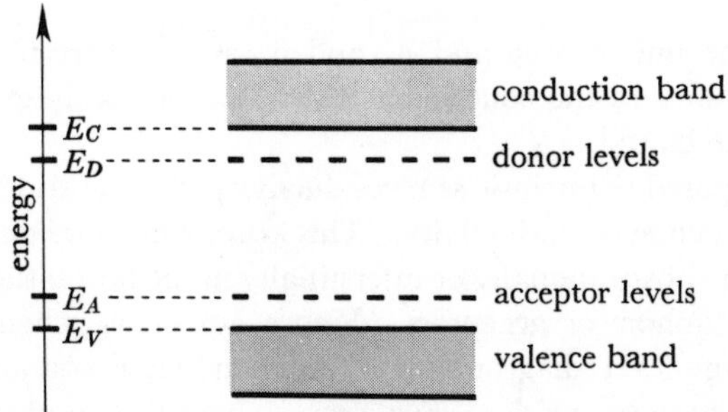

Figure 3-8 *Possible band diagram for intrinsic semiconductor containing both donors and acceptors.*

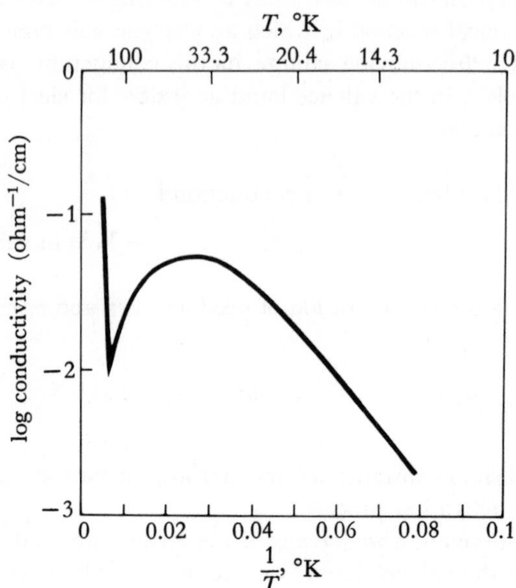

Figure 3-9 *Conductivity of a semiconductor containing impurities.*

general case of an intrinsic semiconductor the specific conductivity σ is given by the equation

$$\sigma = ne\mu_n + pe\mu_p$$

where e is the unit charge and μ_n and μ_p are the carrier mobilities. Usually, mobility in the conduction band is appreciably greater than in the valence band.

As opposed to intrinsic semiconductivity, there is also "extrinsic" or impurity-type semiconductivity. This arises when foreign atoms are present either substitutionally or interstitially in the host lattice and can act either as donors or acceptors. Figure 3-8 shows schematically a possible energy-level diagram for a semiconductor containing both n-type and p-type impurities. For a case where the number of donor centers exceeds the number of acceptor centers, the number of electrons excited to the conduction band is proportional to the Boltzmann distribution factor between the donor levels and the conduction band. Thus

$$n \propto e^{-(E_C - E_D)/kT}$$

Assuming that mobility is temperature-independent, so that σ is proportional to n, the excitation energy $(E_C - E_D)$ can be obtained from the slope of the plot of the log of the conductivity vs. reciprocal temperature. For the case in which the number of acceptor centers exceeds the number of donor centers, the situation is similar and differs only in that the excitation energy for the p-type carriers is $E_A - E_V$. In both cases, the impurity center which is present in smaller concentration is effectively destroyed by transfer of electrons from the donor to the acceptor centers.

Figure 3-9 gives a plot of the log of the conductivity as a function of reciprocal temperature for a typical n-type semiconductor. At low temperature the conductivity is low but increases logarithmically as electrons are excited from the donor centers to the conduction band. When the temperature is high enough that all the donors are ionized, the

Table 3-6 *Carrier characteristics in Si and Ge semiconductors (in ev)*

		Silicon	Germanium
Band gap		1.21	0.75
Carrier mobility			
electrons		1300 [a]	3800 [a]
holes		500 [a]	1800 [a]
Energy, $E_C - E_D$	P	0.045	0.01
	As	0.049	0.01
	Sb	0.039	0.01
	Au	0.85	0.70
Energy, $E_A - E_V$	B	0.045	0.01
	Al	0.057	0.01
	Ga	0.065	0.01
	In	0.16	0.01
	Zn	0.092, 0.3	0.03, 0.10
	Fe	0.5	0.34
	Mn	0.5	0.08, 0.38

[a] In units of cm^2/volt sec.

conductivity drops with rising temperature because of increased lattice scattering. In this region, called the "exhaustion" region, behavior is essentially metallic. At still higher temperatures, conductivity rises again, as excitation occurs from the valence band to the conduction band. In other words, the material behaves as an intrinsic semiconductor.

A summary of some representative semiconductor characteristics is given in Table 3-6.

• 3-6 Magnetic Properties of Solids

The most familiar class of magnetic behavior is that referred to as ferromagnetism, with its characteristic features of large positive susceptibility, which is not independent of the magnetic field, and permanent magnetization, which persists after removal of the field (hysteresis). Iron, cobalt, and nickel are the only elements ferromagnetic at room temperature; several others, including Gd and Dy, become so at lower temperature. Furthermore, a number of compounds—e.g., Fe_3O_4, Mn_4N, CrTe, CrO_2—and many alloys—e.g., Alnico (Al, Ni, Co), Heusler alloys of the type Cu, Mn, Al—are ferromagnetic.

The requirements for the occurrence of ferromagnetism are the presence of paramagnetic cations and sufficiently strong interactions between them to produce domains of parallel-aligned magnetic moments. The magnetism of a ferromagnetic material arises from the electron spin moment rather than from the orbital moment, the latter being quenched by interactions with the crystal field. The spin alignment that produces a domain might be envisioned as being analogous to the parallel spin alignment found in molecules such as O_2. In this molecule there are two spins corresponding to two unpaired electrons, one each in separate antibonding orbitals. By having the electrons in separate orbitals, the Coulomb repulsion energy is minimized. This is ensured by the electrons having the same spin, so that by the Pauli principle they cannot be in the same orbital.

In an analogous way, unpaired electrons localized on the cations of a metallic solid will under certain circumstances be aligned parallel. The circumstances required are: (1) that there be enough near-neighbors (eight or more); (2) that the localized unpaired electron be sufficiently clear of the nucleus (i.e., the wave function have low amplitude near the nucleus, as would be true for *d* or *f* electrons); and (3) that the internuclear distance be neither so short as to produce electron-pair bond formation nor so large as to lose all electron correlation. In practice, the first two requirements are met by most of the transition elements; the third requirement, by Fe, Co, Ni, and some lanthanides.

The spin alignment of ferromagnetism can be destroyed by raising the temperature sufficiently. The critical temperature, above which behavior is typical of a normal paramagnetic material, is the so-called Curie temperature. Only below this temperature can domains exist. A ferromagnetic material below its Curie temperature already has domains of the order of 10^{-2} to 10^{-5} cm across, even though the sample as a whole may appear to be demagnetized. This is due to cancellation of the individual domain moments, caused by their random alignment with respect to each other. Upon application of an external magnetic field, the properly aligned domains increase at the expense of the improperly aligned ones; thus, a net moment is generated.

Antiferromagnetism is believed to arise when antiparallel spin arrangement results from magnetic ion interaction. It occurs most commonly in materials in which nonmagnetic atoms such as oxygens occur between the magnetic ions and act as intermediate coupling agents. As a specific example, in the case of MnO, the magnetic moment of one Mn^{++} ion is opposed to that of near-neighbor Mn^{++} ions, separated by oxygen atoms.

In the ferrites, materials of formula $MO \cdot Fe_2O_3$ (M = Mn, Co, Ni, Cu, Mg, Zn, Cd, Fe^{++}, etc.) having spinel structure, a combination of magnetic interactions occurs, leading to commercially important magnetic materials. The structure of ferrites can be considered to have two sublattices, A and B, one consisting of tetrahedral sites and the other of octahedral sites. The magnetic moments of the atoms on the A sublattice interact antiferromagnetically with the moments on the B sublattice. The net result is that the A atoms are thus aligned parallel amongst themselves, as are the B atoms amongst themselves. If the moment of the A atom is equal to the moment of the B atom, the magnetization cancels and the result is antiferromagnetism. If, however, one moment exceeds the other, the net magnetization does not cancel and the material is sometimes said to be *ferrimagnetic*, although operationally its behavior is of course ferromagnetic.

• 3-7 Defect Solid State

The term *defect solid state* is applied to those solids in which the order is not complete, either because of irregularity in the arrangement of

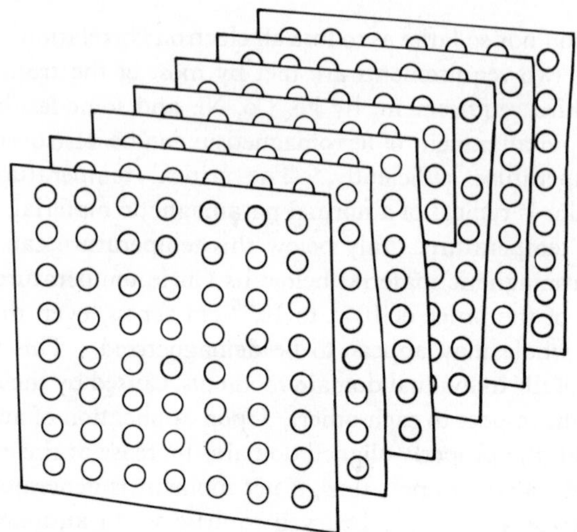

Figure 3-10 *Representation of edge dislocation.*

units—e.g., vacancies, interstitial atoms, dislocations—or because of substitution of one kind of species for another—e.g., impurity atoms, *F* centers. Defects are often of particular interest to the chemist since they may lead to nonstoichiometric compounds by one or the other or both of the above types of disorder.

Because of entropy, at any temperature above absolute zero, it is probable to have some of the atoms displaced from normal lattice sites to interstitial positions and also to have some of the atoms moved from normal lattice sites in the interior of the crystal to regular positions on the surface.

The first type of defect is called a Frenkel defect and can be considered to consist of an interstitial atom plus a lattice vacancy. The second type of defect is called a Schottky defect and can be considered to consist of a cation vacancy plus an anion vacancy. Frenkel defects are favored for small cations in combination with highly polarizable anions. Thus, AgBr, for example, has relatively many interstitial Ag^+ ions, increasing from 0.076 per cent at 210°C to 0.4 per cent at 300°C. Schottky defects are favored when the ions are more nearly equal in size, because the interstitial positions are apt to be too small for easy occupancy, and when the anions are not especially polarizable. The latter would be advantageous for relieving ion-ion repulsion in the interstitial case. In general, the concentration of Schottky defects in ionic crystals is too low to affect the measured density, but in some cases—e.g., δ-TiO with 15 per cent of the sites vacant—the difference is measurable. Frenkel and Schottky defects are useful as ways of accounting for self-diffusion and ionic conductivity in crystalline solids.

Dislocations, as opposed to the point defects mentioned above, are line defects in the sense that they involve lines of atoms misaligned with respect to some of their neighbors. The two major kinds are edge dislocations and screw dislocations. An edge dislocation may be visualized as the misalignment at the edge of a lattice plane inserted part way into a crystal, as shown in Figure 3-10. Far from the edge dislocation, the lattice periodicity is normal; at the edge itself, there is considerable strain. With a screw dislocation, the line of atoms misaligned with respect to some of their neighbors represents an axis about which the crystal planes are warped to give an effect not unlike the threads of a screw. In other words, what would constitute a roundtrip in a perfectly regular lattice results, with a screw dislocation, to a displacement to the lattice plane above.

In a specific case, as represented in Figure 3-11, where the screw axis is parallel to the c direction, n steps in the a direction followed by m

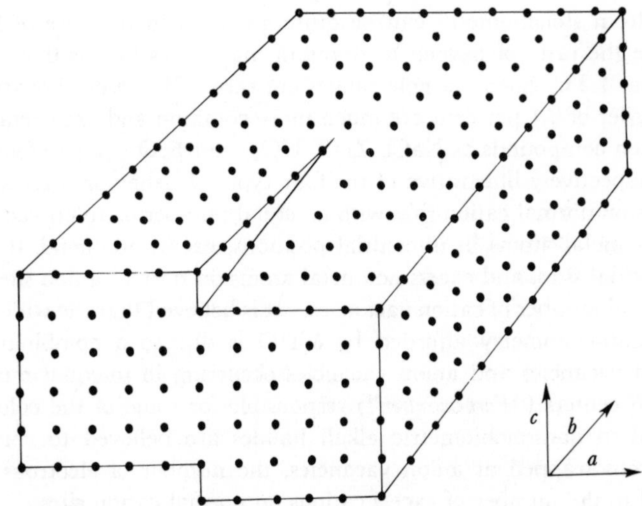

***Figure 3-11** Representation of screw dislocation.*

steps in the b direction, then n steps in the $-a$ direction, and finally m steps in the $-b$ direction will not return to the original lattice point but to the lattice point directly above the start. It is believed that the existence of dislocations in crystals is of major significance in determining solid-state properties, including bulk properties such as conductivity and mechanical strength and surface properties such as crystal growth and catalysis.

Impurities, as a type of defect, are almost impossible to avoid because of the difficulty of preparing chemicals purer than 10^{-6} mole per cent of extraneous material. Substitutional impurities, such as B in Ge or $CaCl_2$ in NaCl, will markedly affect conductivity. In the first case, boron with three valence electrons contributes a "hole" to the germanium valence band; in the second case, inclusion of Ca^{++} at a Na^+ site in the NaCl structure requires by electrical neutrality a cation vacancy at another site. Just as a neighboring electron is mobile in moving into the "hole" of the germanium valence band, an adjacent Na^+ ion is mobile when it moves into the cation vacancy. It should be noted that impurity atoms may also occupy interstitial sites. An interesting example is copper in PbS, where interstitial copper atoms act as donor centers but Cu substituted for lead acts as an acceptor center.

Nonstoichiometry, defined as deviation from integral atomic ratios, can be regarded as an example of impurity defects. The deviation from stoichiometry can be quite great, as in the case of δ-TiO, where the ratio of oxygen to titanium may be as low as 0.69 and as high as 1.33. Such extreme ranges are rare. However, deviations of the order of 0.1 per cent are much more common and are exemplified by such compounds as NaCl, ZnO, UO_2, and FeO. These four cases are respectively illustrative of the four types of behavior: excess metal atoms on normal cation sites with an equal number of anion vacancies, excess metal atoms in interstitial positions, excess nonmetal atoms in interstitial sites, and excess nonmetal atoms on normal anion sites with an equal number of cation vacancies. It is believed that the wide range of nonstoichiometry afforded by δ-TiO is due to a combination of cation vacancies and anion vacancies occurring in unequal numbers. The F centers ("*Farbenzentren*") responsible for some of the colors observed in nonstoichiometric alkali halides are believed to consist of electrons trapped at anion vacancies, the number of electrons being equal to the number of excess cations on normal cation sites.

• 3-8 Luminescence

The term *luminescence* is applied to the delayed emission of electromagnetic radiation after excitation by a means such as ultraviolet light or particle bombardment. If the emission is immediate (less than 10^{-8} sec), the process can be called *fluorescence;* if delayed, *phosphorescence.* The mechanism is essentially the same and can be formulated as three steps: absorption of energy, storage of energy, and re-emission.

In solids the primary absorption can occur (case 1) by excitation of an electron from the valence band to the conduction band or (case 2) by excitation of an impurity atom to a higher electronic state. The storage can occur in case 1 by trapping of the conduction electron at an impurity center, or for case 2 by degrading the energy through vibration to an excited state whose transition to the ground state is "forbidden." Re-emission can occur in case 1 when a trapped electron recombines with the "hole" in the valence band, or in case 2 by return to the ground state after re-excitation of vibrational levels of the upper electronic state. In the latter case, final emission need not occur from the same atom which absorbed the primary energy, since it is possible to have transfer of energy between impurity centers. For example, in some "fluorescent lights," absorption of energy at Mn^{++} centers results in emission from Sb^{+3} centers, the energy transfer being possible because the emission band of Mn^{++} overlaps the absorption band of Sb^{+3}.

• Supplementary Reading

In addition to other monographs of this series, the following references should prove helpful:

1. W. F. de Jong, "General Crystallography," Freeman, San Francisco, 1959.
2. C. Kittel, "Introduction to Solid State Physics," 2nd ed., Wiley, New York, 1956.
3. A. F. Wells, "Structural Inorganic Chemistry," 3rd ed., Clarendon Press, Oxford, 1962.
4. N. Cusack, "The Electrical and Magnetic Properties of Solids," Longmans, Green, London, 1958.
5. P. Pringsheim, "Fluorescence and Phosphorescence," Interscience, New York, 1949.

4

Liquids and Solutions

The structure of liquids is considerably more difficult to ascertain than that of solids, since the correlation in space characteristic of solids is only vestigial in liquids and even that residue is subject to large fluctuations in time.

• 4-1 Structure of Liquids

X-ray analysis of liquids reveals the existence of preferred spacing distances which show up as maxima in a radial distribution curve such as the one in Figure 4-1. The ordinate represents the probability of finding another atom in a volume element at a distance r from a particular reference atom. The fact that there is zero probability at short distances is due to volume exclusion by impenetrability of atoms.

The sharpness of the first maximum suggests that a first coordination sphere is fairly well defined. The less pronounced character of the succeeding maxima indicates a washing-out of structure. Eventually at large r, the curve sweeps upward, as expected for completely random distribution. Normalization to random distribution allows a calculation of the number of atoms in each coordination shell. The values for nearest-neighbors so obtained for monatomic liquids just

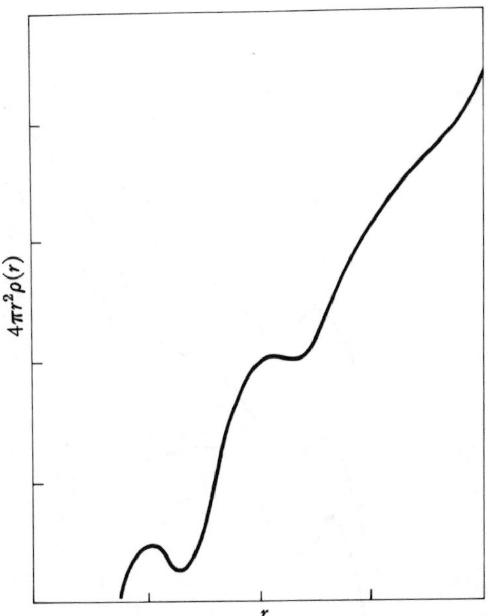

Figure 4-1 *Radial distribution curve of a liquid.*

above the melting point usually lie between 8 and 12. Specifically, there are 10.6 for Al, 10.2 to 10.9 for Ar, 8 for K, and 9.8 for Li. Close-packing of spheres would correspond to 12 nearest-neighbors, but random motion would tend to reduce this number.

Large numbers of near-neighbors are expected only when there is little directional bonding. If there is spatial preference due to localized interaction, either because of electrostatic attraction between oppositely charged ions or because of covalent bond formation, then in general the number of nearest-neighbors is reduced. In the case of molten salts the number of nearest-neighbors is limited by their tendency to be oppositely charged. For covalent molecules—e.g., Cl_2—the number of nearest-neighbors is limited by saturation of covalence. Thus, in liquid Cl_2 there is only one near-neighbor for each atom, and the second coordination shell has significantly fewer atoms than the number that would correspond to close-packing of spherical Cl_2 molecules.

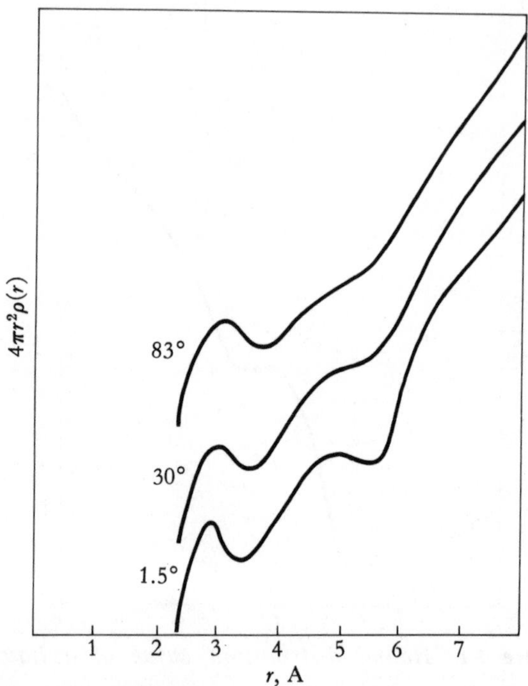

Figure 4-2 *Radial distribution curves for water. (Higher temperature curves have been displaced upward.)*

Whereas H_2S molecules are essentially close-packed, H_2O molecules in liquid water are far from close-packed. Figure 4-2 shows the radial distribution curves in liquid water at several different temperatures. Because the scattering power of H atoms for X rays is much less than that of oxygen atoms, the radial distribution curves given apply to oxygen-atom positions only. Significant features of the curves include the decided maximum at 2.9 to 3.0 A and less pronounced ones at about 5 and 7 A. The integrated area under the sharp maximum corresponds to about 4.5 near-neighbors. As the temperature is raised from 1.5 to 83°C, the nearest-neighbor maximum shifts to larger distance and broadens, with total area increasing to indicate approximately five nearest-neighbors. The second and third maxima show a more drastic temperature dependence and essentially disappear at higher temperatures.

• 4-2 Structure of Water

The radial distribution curves of water can be accounted for by postulating a structure similar to that of ice. The four nearest-neighbors in ice (Figure 4-3) correspond to tetrahedrally disposed oxygen atoms. In the tetrahedral unit, hydrogen bonding is postulated between the oxygen atom at the center of the tetrahedron and those at the corners. This geometry is not unexpected because, of the four sp^3 hybrid orbitals assigned to the oxygen, the two which contain "lone pair" electrons can form hydrogen bonds at tetrahedral angles to the two which covalently bond hydrogen atoms. Owing to proton motion it is not possible to distinguish between the covalently and the hydrogen-bonded positions.

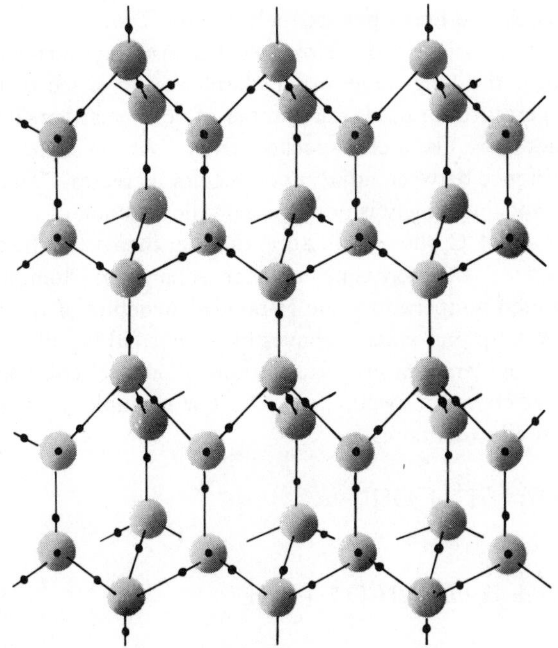

Figure 4-3 *Ice structure.*

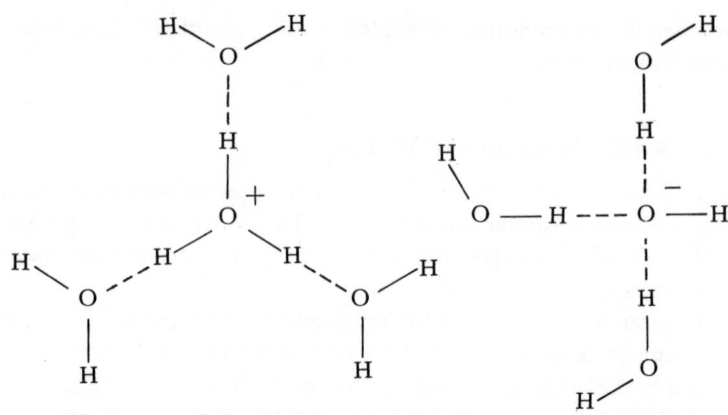

Figure 4-4 Possible structures of $H_9O_4^+$ and $H_7O_4^-$.

Figure 4-3 represents one possible placement of the protons consistent with H_2O stoichiometry.

It is believed that when ice melts the short-range order described above is largely maintained. However, because the short-range order is not perfect, the long-range order characteristic of ice is destroyed. As the temperature is raised, the number of near-neighbors increases—i.e., becomes more like a close-packed array. At the same time, however, the distance between adjacent molecules increases. Thus it is not surprising that the density is not a monotonic function of temperature. Between 0° and 4°C, the coordination number increase is the dominant factor; above 4°C, increasing nuclear separation dominates. At sufficiently high temperatures the H-bonded structure of water is completely broken up and water behaves like a normal liquid.

The low-temperature association of water complicates the description of common species in H_2O. For example, the dissociation of water, usually written as

$$H_2O \rightleftharpoons H^+ + OH^-$$

or

$$H_2O + H_2O \rightleftharpoons H_3O^+ + OH^-$$

is considerably more complex than shown. One suggestion which emphasizes the complexity of the problem postulates that the corresponding species are $H_9O_4^+$ and $H_7O_4^-$. Possible structures for these are shown in Figure 4-4. They have been formulated on the basis of conductivity experiments in conjunction with observations on acidity functions.

• 4-3 Liquid Ammonia

Ammonia is an associated solvent like water except that the tendency toward order is less in NH_3. One reason for this is the geometry of the NH_3 molecule, which corresponds to one lone pair of electrons in the apex position of a pyramid. (The molecule can also be visualized as a tetrahedral unit with a N in the center, three covalently bound H's, and one lone pair directed tetrahedrally.) As a consequence, a single ammonia molecule can bond to but one additional H atom. Even though its three H atoms can bind to additional nitrogen atoms, it necessarily follows that the original NH_3 molecule cannot be a member of more than one hydrogen-bonded ring. As a result, unlike the case of water, ammonia cannot form an extended three-dimensional network. At best, branched string-like structures may exist. Also, because of the reduced electronegativity of nitrogen, the hydrogen bonds in NH_3 are considerably weaker than those in water, so that association is less pronounced.

The properties of liquid ammonia in comparison to those of liquid water and also HF are shown in Table 4-1. The short liquid

Table 4-1 *Properties of liquids*

Property	NH_3	H_2O	HF
Melting point, °C	−77.74	0	−92.3
Boiling point, °C	−33.35	100	19.4
Density at b.p., g/cc	0.677	0.958	0.987
Viscosity, poise	0.0025(−33.4°)	0.0028(100°)	
Surface tension, erg/cm²	35.14(−33.4°)	58.85(100°)	8.65(19.4°)
Equivalent conductance, ohm⁻¹	5×10^{-9}(−33.4°)	6×10^{-8}(25°)	1.4×10^{-5}(−15°)
Heat of vaporization, kcal/mole	5.64	9.72	7.24
Dielectric constant	22(−33.4°)	87.8(0°)	83.6(0°)
Ion product	1×10^{-28}	1.0×10^{-14}	

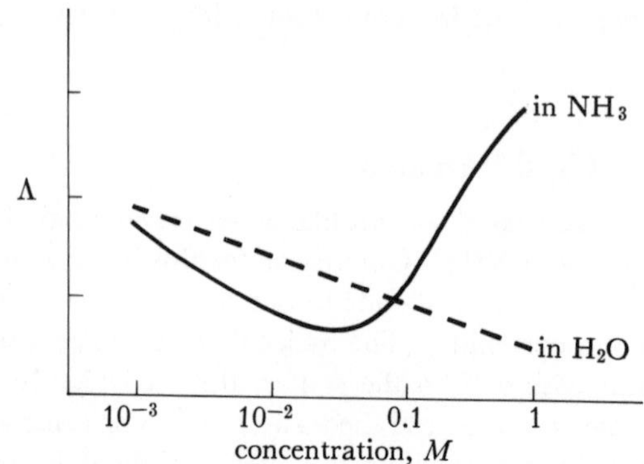

***Figure 4-5** Equivalent conductance of KBr.*

range of NH_3 compared to H_2O and HF might be attributed to the fact that the NH_3 molecule is more spherical. (Short liquid ranges are generally characteristic of nonassociated spherical molecules.) Also, not only is the density of liquid NH_3 considerably below that of H_2O, but NH_3 shows a large thermal coefficient, which suggests absence of compensating effects as are found in H_2O.

As a solvent, NH_3 resembles H_2O in being able to dissolve ionic solids. This is largely due to the appreciable dielectric constant, which serves to reduce the interionic attractions. However, the fact that the dielectric constant is much less than that of H_2O shows up in the solution properties. For example, as shown in Figure 4-5, the conductivity behavior in liquid NH_3 may deviate markedly from that in water. At low concentrations the behavior is much like that in water, but at higher concentrations there appears a minimum in conductance followed by a marked rise. The minimum has been attributed to ion association in liquid NH_3 caused by the lower dielectric constant. Support for this interpretation comes from measurements of freezing-point lowering. Figure 4-6 is a plot of freezing-point lowering as a function of concentration. There is a decided decrease in the apparent number of particles per mole as the concentration of KBr in NH_3 is increased. A decrease in the number of particles can be brought about by formation of K^+Br^- ion pairs and also by formation of triplets such as $Br^-K^+Br^-$. Thus, as KBr concentration is increased, nonconducting ion pairs give way to charged triplets, so that the conductivity increases. It should be noted that 2KBr and K^+ plus KBr_2^- correspond to the same solute particle concentration. Therefore, at high concentrations the freezing-point lowering is equivalent to that for no dissociation.

Besides the appreciable dielectric constant of NH_3, another reason for solubility of salts in liquid ammonia is the tendency of NH_3 to complex with metal cations. Because NH_3 is a stronger Lewis base than is H_2O, it has greater ability to solvate cations. However, it apparently does not interact well with anions. As a result, a variety of cations form liquid NH_3 solutions but only the larger, lower-charged anions do so. Higher-charged anions or small anions are more likely to correspond to high lattice energies, thereby making it more difficult for the cation solvation energy to compensate. As a typical example of the disparity in water and ammonia solubility, the solubility of AgI in liquid NH_3 is more than 100 times that of NaF in NH_3.

An unusual aspect of NH_3 as a solvent is its ability to dissolve alkali and some other metals without evolution of hydrogen to give solutions which upon evaporation restore the metal. As a specific example, 10.7 gram-atoms of sodium can be dissolved in 1000 g of NH_3 at $-33.8°C$. The dilute solutions are blue; the concentrated, bronze.

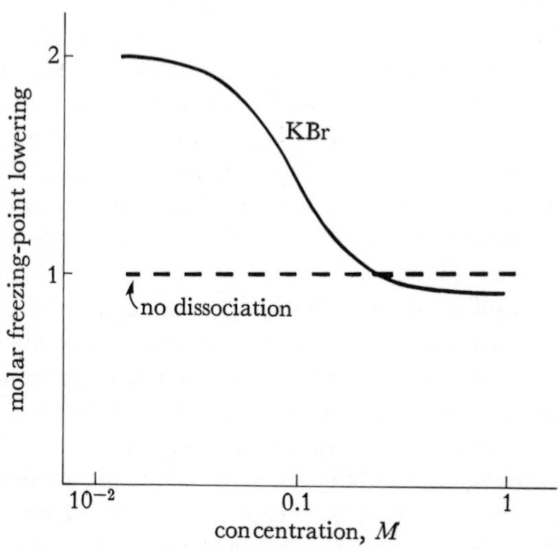

Figure 4-6 *Freezing-point lowering of NH_3 by KBr.*

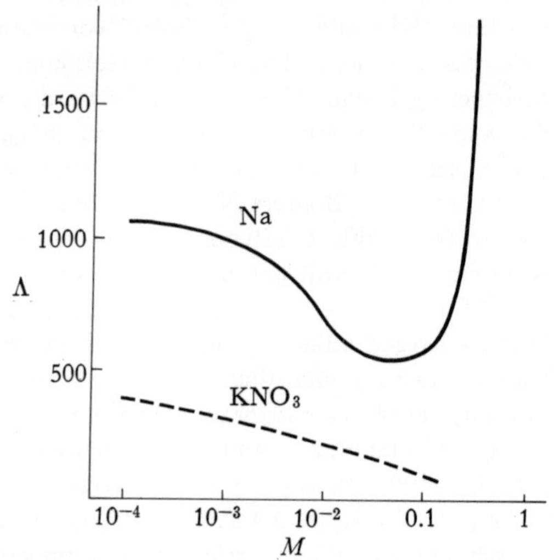

Figure 4-7 Conductivity of Na in liquid NH_3.

At temperatures below $-42°$, there is separation into two liquid phases, one blue and the other bronze. Conductivity of sodium-NH_3 solutions is represented in Figure 4-7 as a function of concentration.

In dilute solutions the behavior is salt-like, in that the molar conductance is of the same order of magnitude as KNO_3 and decreases with increasing concentration. It is believed that in dilute solution the sodium is dissociated into Na^+ ion and a solvated electron. In concentrated solutions the conductivity becomes enormous, approaching an equivalent conductance value of 8×10^4 ohm^{-1} cm^2 per gram-atom of Na at saturation. (This compares to a value of 5×10^6 ohm^{-1} cm^2 per gram-atom of solid sodium.) Such large conductivity cannot be explained by ionic migration but requires delocalization of the electronic wave functions as in metals. Besides the color and the conductivity, the surface tension of Na-NH_3 solutions also shows a decided transition from salt-like behavior to that expected for metals.

The magnetic susceptibility of metal-ammonia solutions generally supports the above picture but suggests a complication in the intermediate concentration range. For dilute solutions, the observed magnetic moment extrapolates to one electron spin per sodium. For concentrated solutions, especially near saturation, the susceptibility behavior is similar to that of an electron gas in a metal—that is, the susceptibility is small, positive, and temperature-independent. In the intermediate region the susceptibility is less than at either extreme of concentration and, in fact, it becomes negative at sufficiently low temperature. The minimum in the susceptibility has been taken to indicate that electron pairs are formed in metal-ammonia solutions. From the temperature coefficient, the pairing energy is estimated to be 4 to 5 kcal per mole of electron pairs.

Pure ammonia, like pure water, has a small but finite electrical conductivity. In the case of ammonia, this is attributed to a dissociation of the type

$$2NH_3 \rightleftharpoons NH_4^+ + NH_2^-$$

for which the ion product has been estimated to be 1×10^{-28}. As in water, the actual species are no doubt more complicated than those shown in the equation. By analogy with water, any substance increasing the NH_4^+ concentration in ammonia represents an acid in the ammonia system; any substance increasing NH_2^-, a base. Thus acid-base reactions are possible, as for example,

$$Zn(NH_2)_2 + 2NH_4NO_3 \rightarrow Zn(NO_3)_2 + 4NH_3$$

$$Zn(NH_2)_2 + 2NaNH_2 \rightarrow Na_2Zn(NH_2)_4$$

These reactions illustrate incidentally the amphoteric nature of zinc amide in ammonia.

• 4-4 Liquid Hydrogen Fluoride

The structure of liquid HF is not known, though in the solid and in the gaseous phases there is evidence supporting linear polymers in which the F atoms form a zig-zag chain held together by hydrogen bonds. It would be reasonable to suppose therefore that the liquid contains similar polymeric species. Like NH_3 but unlike H_2O, the polymers are prevented by molecular geometry from being three-dimensional networks. Instead they are chains or perhaps rings. The latter would be consistent with the relatively small surface tension (Table 4-1) and its relatively small temperature dependence. However, it would appear inconsistent with the observed high dielectric constant. Most probably, liquid hydrogen fluoride is a mixture of a variety of species—some strings and some rings.

As a solvent, liquid HF is able to dissolve more different materials than either H_2O or NH_3. However, "dissolve" in HF usually means chemical reaction with formation of anions and cations other than those expected. In general, no matter what the apparent solute anion before solution, the major anion in the final solution will be F^- (perhaps better written as HF_2^-). This comes about because F^- in HF is a poorer base than most other substances. When most solutes are placed in HF, protons are transferred from HF to the anions to form either neutral species, which are frequently expelled, or positive species. Some illustrative examples are

$$NaCl(s) + HF \rightarrow HCl(g) + Na^+ + F^-$$

$$NaBr(s) + HF \rightarrow HBr(g) + Na^+ + F^-$$

$$KCN(s) + HF \rightarrow HCN(g) + K^+ + F^-$$

$$NaN_3(s) + HF \rightarrow HN_3(g) + Na^+ + F^-$$

$$NaOH(s) + 2HF \rightarrow H_3O^+ + Na^+ + 2F^-$$

$$KNO_3(s) + 2HF \rightarrow H_2NO_3^+ + K^+ + 2F^-$$

$$H_2O + HF \rightarrow H_3O^+ + F^-$$

$$Na_2CO_3(s) + 3HF \rightarrow CO_2(g) + H_3O^+ + 2Na^+ + 3F^-$$

Perchlorates are probably an exception to the general rule that all anions are converted by liquid HF. At least in concentrated perchlorate solutions the conductivity indicates that some of the perchlorate remains anionic.

• 4-5 Hydration

The study of nonaqueous systems has uncovered a host of interesting phenomena; however, the fact remains that aqueous systems still present major unsolved problems, which are unique to H_2O and probably will be understood only by study of the aqueous solutions themselves. The problems can be classified in two categories: (1) What happens to the solvent? (2) What happens to the solute when the solution is finally formed?

An informative method of attack is to consider the thermodynamics of solution formation. For the general case of dissolving a solute in water the total free-energy change can be considered to be composed of the solute vaporization (e.g., lattice free energy for a solid) followed by the hydration of the vaporized solute (e.g., solvation free energy of ions). If the free-energy change corresponds to standard-state conditions—1 atm pressure for perfect gases, ideal 1 *m* solutions, and 25°C—then the values are standard free energies, $\Delta F°$. Because the effects due to the enthalpy term ($\Delta H°$) and the entropy term ($-T\,\Delta S°$) often cancel, it is informative to consider separately the enthalpy and the entropy changes accompanying the steps of the solution cycle. The cycle for the specific case of an ionic solid as solute is shown in (I).

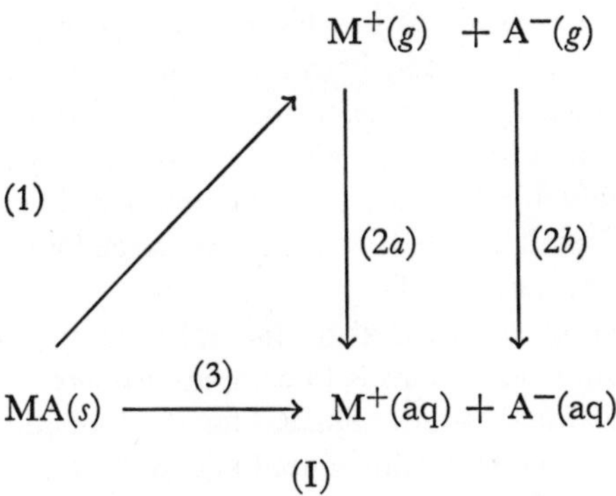

(I)

For either the enthalpy or the entropy change, the total process (3) must equal the sum of (1) and (2). As for enthalpy, step (1) is the lattice energy, which can be calculated as discussed in Chapter 3 (corrected for $P\,\Delta V$ work at 25°C by addition of $2RT$). Step (3) is the heat of solution, which can be determined experimentally from the temperature coefficient of solubility. The difference between step (3) and step (1) gives the total heat of hydration for the cation and the anion.

$$\Delta H°_{\text{solution}} - \Delta H°_{\text{lattice}} = \Delta H°_{\text{hydration}}$$

Although it is reasonable to assume that the total hydration enthalpy is a simple sum of cation and anion contributions, there is no direct thermodynamic way of separating the two. Instead, various methods have been devised for calculating either a reference value for one ion or for dividing the measured values between the cation and anion of a given pair.

Most methods make use of the Born equation,

$$-\Delta F^\circ = \frac{Ne^2}{2r}\left(1 - \frac{1}{D}\right)$$

which gives the free-energy difference between the charging of N spheres of radius r and charge e in a vacuum and in a medium of dielectric constant D. The application of this equation to the hydration process has been criticized on the ground that water is not a continuous dielectric and, furthermore, that the radius r is not the crystal radius. In fact, there is a question as to what r really means, especially in the gas phase. It is evident that, because of the form of the dependence on dielectric constant, the actual value of D used is not critical; however, the implication that the detailed structure of solvated ions can be ignored is questionable. In any case, the problem should be less severe for large ions of small charge. It is on these large ions that most ionic-energy assignments are based.

The general problem then for splitting up thermodynamic values between individual ions is to compare *measured* values for a pair of ions with individual values *calculated* for the individual (large) ions. To compare measured hydration enthalpies (ΔH°'s) with the quantities calculated from the Born equation (ΔF°'s), it is necessary to have hydration entropies. These can be obtained as the difference between calculated entropies of gas ions and measured entropies of ions in solution. For a monatomic gas in its electronic ground state the entropy is given by the Sackur-Tetrode equation,

$$S = 2.303R(\tfrac{3}{2}\log M + \tfrac{5}{2}\log T - \log P + \log g - 0.5055)$$

where R is the gas constant, M is the atomic weight, T is the temperature, P is the pressure, and g is the multiplicity $(2J + 1)$. The entropy in solution for a given pair of ions can be obtained by measuring the entropy change for a reaction yielding the pair of ions—e.g., by measuring the thermal coefficient of solubility or the thermal coefficient of a galvanic cell. The entropy change for a reaction, when added to the absolute entropy of the solid reactants (known from the third law), gives the total absolute entropy of the pair of ions in the solution.

In summary, from the Sackur-Tetrode equation we can calculate the entropy of $M^+(g)$ and the entropy of $A^-(g)$; from thermodynamic measurements we can get the sum of the total entropies of M^+(aq) and A^-(aq); the difference corresponds to the entropy change for the hydration of the pair of ions M^+ and A^-. Since the enthalpy of hydration for the pair of ions is known from the enthalpy cycle, the two ($\Delta H°$ and $\Delta S°$) can be combined to give the free energy of hydration for the pair. It is this free energy which, through use of the Born equation, is split up between the cation and the anion.

The most frequently quoted hydration parameters are those assigned by Latimer, who assumed that the only modification needed in the Born equation was an additive factor for the crystal radius. It was found that addition of 0.85 A to crystal radii of Pauling for alkali-metal cations and addition of 0.10 A for halide anions gave effective radii which apparently satisfied the Born equation. Sums of ± pairs so calculated agreed satisfactorily with the free energies of hydration based on measured values. Table 4-2 contains values of $\Delta F°$ for the hydration of some common univalent ions as assigned by Latimer and co-workers. Included also are values of the enthalpy and the entropy of hydration. These were obtained as follows. If the Born equation

Table 4-2 *Ion hydration parameters*

Ion	$-\Delta F°$, kcal/mole	$-\Delta H°$, kcal/mole	$-\Delta S°$, cal/mole/deg
Li^+	115	121	22
Na^+	90	95	17
K^+	74	76	8
Rb^+	68	69	6
Cs^+	61	62	4
F^-	114	123	29
Cl^-	84	89	15
Br^-	78	81	12
I^-	70	72	7

is differentiated with respect to temperature, the result suggests a linear dependence of $\Delta S°$ on reciprocal effective radius. Values of $\Delta S°$ have been picked so as to give the best fit for such a linear plot. Of course, $\Delta H°$ values are obtained by difference, using $T = 298°K$.

It must be noted that although the $\Delta H°$ values are commonly used as given in Table 4-2 the $\Delta S°$ values in general use are not those listed. The reason for this is that it has proved more convenient to call the entropy of the H^+ ion in aqueous solution zero and thereby define it as a standard. Fortunately, the two scales differ but slightly and, furthermore, $T\,\Delta S°$ is usually small compared to $\Delta H°$. (To add to the confusion, in some places the convention is adopted that the enthalpy, $H°$, of the H^+ ion in aqueous solution is also taken as zero. This is 108 kcal per mole lower than that obtained using H_2 as the reference of zero enthalpy and the hydration enthalpy change, $\Delta H°$, consistent with the values in Table 4.2.)

Values quoted in Table 4-3 are based on zero entropy for H^+ in aqueous solution. The table also lists heats of hydration for various common ions. All values are based on National Bureau of Standards tables; entropies of gaseous ions have been obtained from the Sackur-Tetrode equation correcting only for ground-state multiplicity of the ion. The latter may be one or two entropy units too low for ions of transition elements in which excited electronic states may be populated.

From the values in Table 4-3 it can be seen that the heats of hydration increase drastically with ionic charge. Thus, for +1 ions, $\Delta H°$ (kcal per mole) is about -100; for +2, about -400; for +3, about -1000. The increase is approximately that predicted by the Born equation—i.e., proportional to the square of the charge. Furthermore, the heats decrease for ions of larger radius with a given charge. For entropy changes on hydration ($\Delta S° = S°(\text{aq}) - S°(g)$) there are approximately similar trends—viz., +1 ions are about -15 cal per deg per mole; +2, about -55; +3, about -115. The entropy changes seem to depend more on radius and on the sign of the charge than do the enthalpy changes.

The enthalpies and entropies of hydration have been used in drawing conclusions about the structure of water in ionic solutions. For example, the enormous heats of hydration have been taken to indicate formation of strong chemical bonds between an ion and water molecules—i.e., formation of hydrated ions. To estimate the bond energy we first assume a size for the hydrated ion equal to the crystal ionic radius plus the diameter of a water molecule. For the latter we

Table 4-3 Thermodynamic parameters of ions

Ion	$-\Delta H^\circ_{hydration}$	$S^\circ(g)$	$S^\circ(aq)$
H^+	(256) [a]	26.0	(0)
Li^+	121	31.8	3.4
Na^+	95	35.3	14.4
K^+	75	36.9	24.5
Rb^+	69	39.3	29.7
Cs^+	61	40.6	31.8
Mg^{++}	456	35.5	−28.2
Ca^{++}	377	37.0	−13.2
Sr^{++}	342	39.3	−9.4
Ba^{++}	308	40.7	3
Al^{+3}	1109	35.7	−75
Cr^{+3}	1047	40.7	(−74)
Mn^{++}	438	41.5	−20
Fe^{++}	456	42.5	−27.1
Fe^{+3}	1041	41.7	−70.1
Cu^{++}	499	42.1	−23.6
Ag^+	112	40.1	17.7
Zn^{++}	485	38.5	−25.5
Cd^{++}	428	40.1	−14.6
Hg^{++}	(432)	41.8	(−5.4)
Ga^{+3}	1115	38.8	−83
Tl^+	77	41.9	30.4
F^-	121	34.8	−2.3
Cl^-	90	36.3	13.2
Br^-	82	39.2	19.3
I^-	71	40.6	26.1
OH^-	(120)	23.5	−2.5

[a] Values in parentheses are other than N.B.S. values.

can use 3 A, taken from the observed, average X-ray spacing in liquid water. Next we calculate the energy of solvation of the hydrated ion by the rest of the solvent. The Born equation should work well for such a large ion, and it can be used directly to estimate ΔH°, because the associated $T\,\Delta S^\circ$ is relatively small enough to be ignored. The difference between a measured ΔH° of hydration and the value calculated for the hydrated ion is attributed to chemical bonding within the hydrated ion.

For the charge types +1, +2, and +3, this difference comes out to be about 60, 200, and 600 kcal per mole, respectively. Assuming there are on the average six near-neighbors in the first hydration shell, the energy per bond is about 10, 30, and 100 kcal per mole for binding H_2O to +1, +2, and +3 cations, respectively. Certainly the 100 kcal per mole value for the +3 hydration would justify describing the hydrated ion as a real chemical species. Perhaps this is also true for the +2 hydration, but there is a possibility with these hydrated ions of having such rapid exchange of H_2O between the innermost and outer hydration shells that no discrete species can be defined.

Direct kinetic evidence for the existence of definite hydrated species has been supplied in some cases by using O^{18}-labeled water as a tracer in exchange experiments. If H_2O^{18} is added to a solution containing either chromium or aluminum cations and the solvent is sampled (as by distillation) periodically, it is found that the H_2O^{18}/H_2O^{16} ratio decreases with time. For Cr^{+3}, the decrease occurs with a half-time of some 50 hours; for Al^{+3}, of the order of a tenth of a second. In either case, if the isotope ratio is extrapolated back to the time of mixing, it is found that there is instantaneous mixing of the added H_2O^{18} with all the solvent except 6 moles of water per mole of cation. These 6 moles of water constitute the first coordination sphere, and they exchange with the rest of the solvent at the rates noted above.

Unfortunately, most hydrated ions have been found to exchange too fast to be characterized by the isotope dilution method. For these, indirect methods have proved informative in some cases. Most of these methods depend on measurement of a relaxation time—for example, the time required for a nuclear magnetic moment to disorient after alignment by an external magnetic field or the time required for an ion-pairing equilibrium to re-establish after perturbation by an external electric field. Identification of these relaxation times with processes involving exchange of water in the first hydration sphere shows that a number of multiply charged cations retain their hydration shells for times significantly longer than 10^{-8} sec (cf. Section 5-7). In addition, practically all multiply charged cations show in aqueous solutions a Raman spectral line which can be ascribed to a cation-water vibration.

Information concerning structure of aqueous solutions outside the first hydration sphere comes from detailed consideration of hydration entropies. The fact that dissolving has a structural influence beyond the first sphere can be seen from a comparison of the hydration entropy of 1 mole of KCl with that of 2 moles of argon, which is isoelectronic with both K^+ and Cl^-. For the standard states used here, the $\Delta S^\circ_{\text{hydration}}$ in calories per degree per mole (entropy units, or e.u.) is -12.1 and -23.2 for K^+ and Cl^-, respectively, or -35.3 for KCl, compared to $2(-22.2)$, or -44.4, for 2 moles of argon. In both cases, there is apparent over-all ordering on hydration; however, the effect of the ionic charges is to reduce the apparent over-all ordering. To uncover the cause for the difference, it is necessary to analyze the two cases separately, as has been done by H. S. Frank.

When any gas is dissolved in a liquid there is a restriction in the volume accessible to individual molecules. The amount of entropy change associated with this restricting of disorder amounts to approximately -12 e.u. (1 atm gas going to 1 *m* solution). Because the amount of entropy of hydration of 1 mole of argon is -22 e.u., it follows that there must be -10 e.u. associated with the ordering of the water structure. In other words, even a neutral species such as argon has a structure-making effect on liquid water. When the ionic pair K^+ and Cl^- is dissolved in water, there is again expected a change of -12 e.u. for each mole of particles, or -24 e.u. for the pair. Experimentally, however, the hydration entropy is -35 e.u.

In attempting to account for the extra -11 e.u., we consider first the H_2O "frozen" in the first coordination sphere of the ions. For a lower limit it is assumed that there are four H_2O molecules bound to each ion just enough to restrict the molecular motion so as to lose half the entropy of fusion. For 25°C, the molar entropy difference between ice and liquid water is estimated to be 6 e.u. Thus, four H_2O molecules "half-frozen" would give an entropy loss of 12 e.u. for the K^+ ion. Similarly, there would be -12 e.u. for the Cl^- ion.

Second, we need to consider the entropy change associated with the polarization of the dielectric medium outside the first hydration shell. This can be estimated by using the temperature derivative of the Born equation, as done by Latimer, for the radius appropriate to the hydrated ion. This outer-sphere polarization contributes about -5 e.u. for each ion. Thus in attempting to account for the extra -11 e.u., we have succeeded in coming up with -34 e.u. Since this was conservatively estimated, there must be a positive contribution to the entropy which cannot be ignored.

In summary, when an ionic solute is dissolved in water there are not only negative entropy changes associated with restriction of volume, first-sphere hydration, and outer-sphere dielectric polarization but also a positive entropy change which must be assigned to structure-breaking of the solvent. Such structure-breaking can be rationalized by noting that orientation of H_2O molecules in the first hydration sphere must of necessity create a mismatch with respect to perpetuation of the over-all water structure. The magnitude of the mismatch for each ion could be estimated from individual ion hydration entropies, and this would give significant information on solution structure. Attempts have been made, but since these are based on an arbitrary split up of solvation entropy between cation and anion, the detailed conclusions are open to question. However, the effect is real and it seems clear that different ions differ significantly in their structure-breaking ability. In fact, some may even be structure-making, like the rare gases.

• 4-6 Species in Aqueous Solutions

Somewhat less tenuous than the definition of aquo species in aqueous solution is the characterization of solute species independent of aquation. In general, these include complex ions, hydrolyzed species, polymerized species, and ion pairs. Even so, the detailed characterization of solute species is difficult. A large number of diverse techniques are in use which fall in general into one of three classes: thermodynamic, kinetic, or spectral. Examples of the first include electrode potentials, solubilities, vapor pressure, freezing-point lowering, boiling-point elevation, solvent extraction, ion exchange, enthalpy titration, and calorimetry in general. All suffer from complications of solution nonideality. To meet the problem, various assumptions are made concerning the constancy of or the calculability of activity coefficients for individual species. One common assumption, which, however, has been questioned, is that at constant and high salt concentration activity coefficients do not change much with small changes in solution composition.

Kinetic techniques for determining solute species include interpretation, in terms of individual solute species, of reaction rate laws and of transport phenomena such as electrical conductivity, diffusion, and ultracentrifugation. These kinetic methods encounter general complications, as do the thermodynamic methods in dividing bulk behavior of a solution among individual solute species. For example, in interpreting the observed conductivity of a salt solution there is difficulty in separating complex-species formation from effects due to ion-atmosphere drag, viscosity changes, etc.

Of the various methods for detecting formation of new species in solution, it would seem that spectral techniques should be most free of complications. Spectral techniques most commonly used include visible, ultraviolet, or infrared absorption; Raman and Rayleigh scattering; and nuclear magnetic resonance and electron spin resonance absorption. All these phenomena have in common occurrence of an energy-conversion process at a localized center such as afforded by a solute molecule. The process might involve excitation of a bond vibration, orientation of a magnetic dipole, electron excitation, etc. The major problem in all these cases is to identify a particular spectral occurrence with a species of particular structure. In a few favorable cases this can be done strictly on the basis of the spectrum itself. However, in most cases it is necessary to fall back on concentration dependence of spectral intensities. When this is done, the problems of nonideal behavior may again arise.

Table 4-4 is a representative listing of equilibrium constants that characterize species believed to be formed in hydrolytic reactions of cations with water. The constants are concentration constants for the most dilute solutions studied and refer to the reaction

$$M^{+z} + H_2O \rightleftharpoons MOH^{+(z-1)} + H^+$$

with water activity taken as unity. As expected, the trends are that the hydrolyzed species are more stable the higher the ionic charge and the smaller the ion. Also, the transition elements and the post-transition elements hydrolyze more extensively than other ions of similar charge and radius. The reason for this can be interpreted in terms of a higher effective charge, owing to less efficient screening of nuclear charge by *d* electrons.

There are several complications rather common in hydrolysis of positive ions. One involves formation of insoluble hydroxides or basic salts. For example, nearly 0.1 M H^+ is needed to keep appreciable mercuric ion in solution in the absence of complexing anions. Another problem involves hydrolytic polymerization—that is, formation of condensed species containing more than one cation member held together by hydroxy- or possibly oxy-bridges. This process, sometimes called *olation*, is often a slow process and is particularly pronounced

Table 4-4 *Hydrolysis constants at 25°C*

$$K = \frac{[MOH^{+(z-1)}][H^+]}{[M^{+z}]}$$

M^{+z}	log K	M^{+z}	log K
Li^+	−14	PuO_2^{++}	−5.7
Na^+	−15	Mn^{++}	−10
Be^{++}	−6.5	Fe^{++}	−7
Mg^{++}	−12	Fe^{+3}	−2
Ca^{++}	−12.5	Co^{++}	−9
Sr^{++}	−13.2	Co^{+3}	−2
Ba^{++}	−13.4	Ni^{++}	−9
Sc^{+3}	−4.5	Cu^{++}	−8
Y^{+3}	−7	Ag^+	−12
La^{+3}	−8	Zn^{++}	−10
Ce^{+3}	−9	Cd^{++}	−10
Ce^{+4}	0.7	Hg_2^{++}	−5
Zr^{+4}	−0.2	Hg^{++}	−2.8
Th^{+4}	−4	Al^{+3}	−5.0
V^{+3}	−3	Ga^{+3}	−3
Cr^{+3}	−4	In^{+3}	−4
U^{+4}	−0.7	Tl^+	−13
UO_2^{++}	−4.2	Tl^{+3}	−1
Pu^{+3}	−7.0	Sn^{++}	−2
Pu^{+4}	−1.6	Pb^{++}	−7

for ions of high charge. One of the more completely characterized olated species is one of those formed by Cr^{+3}.

$$2Cr(H_2O)_6^{+3} \rightarrow (H_2O)_5Cr(OH)_2Cr(H_2O)_5^{+4} + 2H^+$$

In this species, two OH's serve to bridge together two octahedrally surrounded chromium ions.

A final complication is that many ions hydrolyze further than a single-step. Once the second stage of hydrolysis becomes appreciable, in cases where precipitation or polymerization does not occur, there may be formation of either $M(OH)_2^{+x}$ or MO^{+x}. Because the two species have the same charge and can be considered to differ only in water formulation, they are difficult to distinguish and in fact frequently are considered to be completely equivalent. The problem is the same as that encountered for anions of amphoteric hydroxides, where there is generally a choice between oxyanion and hydroxyanion formulation (e.g., zincate may be written as $ZnO_2^{=}$, $Zn(OH)_4^{=}$, etc.). In certain cases, a distinction between oxy and hydroxy characterization is possible on the basis of kinetic evidence. For example, solutions containing uranyl salts show slow isotope exchange with solvent of two oxygens per uranium. Thus, UO_2^{++} seems a better formulation than $U(OH)_4^{++}$, which *a priori* is equally probable as the product of U^{+6} hydrolysis.

As to the association of complex ions and other ligands, the chemical literature shows that much remains to be done both in filling gaps and resolving contradictory results. One of the most extensive compilations of complex-ion data is found in Special Publications 6 and 7 of the Chemical Society, London, entitled "Stability Constants." Table 4-5 contains a representative sampling of values selected from this compilation. Wherever possible, values were taken which had been extrapolated to zero ionic strength. Differences of ionic environment account for many of the discrepancies between reported values for the same complex. These environmental effects are most serious for the association of highly charged cations and anions. For example, in the case of a $+3$ cation with a -2 anion the ionic-strength effect could change K by as much as three orders of magnitude.

The log K values given in Table 4-5 refer to the addition of one ligand at a time—that is, they are stepwise association constants. In general, the most widespread agreement occurs for the first step, after which the discrepancies due to differences in handling activity coefficients become compounded. Thus, although in some cases it is known that as many as six steps of association occur, there is such wide disagreement concerning the individual constants that no reliable estimate of the K's for all the steps can be given.

Because of the uncertainties in the K values, it is not profitable to attach significance to small differences between K's for different reactions. There are, however, real differences and significant trends within the values. For one thing, the association K for any ligand generally increases with cation charge. For another, the successive addition of ligands in most cases is characterized by lower K values. However, there are departures especially for post-transition elements. Another frequently given generalization is that the association constants with halides for a particular element generally decrease in the

Table 4-5 *Stepwise association constants for complex ions in aqueous solution, 25°C*

$$K = \frac{[ML_n]}{[ML_{n-1}][L]}$$

	log K						
	F^-	Cl^-	Br^-	I^-	SCN^-	NH_3	$SO_4^=$
Be^{++}							
$n = 1$	5.0						
$n = 2$	3.8						
$n = 3$	2.9						
Mg^{++}							
$n = 1$	1.8					0.2	2.2
$n = 2$						−0.2	
$n = 3$						−0.4	
$n = 4$						−0.7	
$n = 5$						−1.0	
$n = 6$						−1.3	
Ca^{++}							
$n = 1$	<1					−0.2	2.3
$n = 2$						−0.6	
$n = 3$						−0.8	
$n = 4$						−1.1	
$n = 5$						−1.3	
$n = 6$						−1.7	
Ba^{++}							
$n = 1$	<0	−0.1					
Sc^{+3}							
$n = 1$	7.1						
$n = 2$	5.8						
$n = 3$	4.5						
$n = 4$	3.5						
La^{+3}							
$n = 1$	3.6	−0.1					3.6
Ce^{+3}							
$n = 1$	4.0	0.1	0.4				3.4
Zr^{+4}							
$n = 1$	8.75	0.30					3.8
$n = 2$	7.3						2.9
$n = 3$	5.8						
Th^{+4}							
$n = 1$	7.6	0.30			1.1		3.3
$n = 2$	5.7						2.4
$n = 3$	4.4						

Table 4-5 *(continued)*

	log K						
	F^-	Cl^-	Br^-	I^-	SCN^-	NH_3	$SO_4^{=}$
Cr^{+3}							
$n = 1$	4.4	0.60			3.1		
$n = 2$	3.3	−0.7			1.7		
$n = 3$	2.5				1.0		
$n = 4$					0.3		
$n = 5$					−0.7		
$n = 6$					−1.6		
U^{+4}							
$n = 1$	9	0.9	0.2		1.5		3.6
$n = 2$					0.6		2.5
UO_2^{++}							
$n = 1$	4.5	0.4	−0.2		0.9		3.0
$n = 2$	3.3						1
$n = 3$	2.6						
$n = 4$	1.3						
Pu^{+3}							
$n = 1$		1.2					1
$n = 2$							0.6
Pu^{+4}							
$n = 1$	7.9	−0.3					3.7
Mn^{++}							
$n = 1$		0					2.3
Fe^{++}							
$n = 1$		0.4			1.0		0.04
$n = 2$		0			−0.9		
Fe^{+3}							
$n = 1$	5.2	1.5	0.60		2.9		4
$n = 2$	3.9	0.7			1.2		1
$n = 3$	2.8	−1			0		
Co^{++}							
$n = 1$		−2.4			3	2.0	2.5
$n = 2$					0	1.5	
$n = 3$					−0.7	0.9	
$n = 4$					0	0.6	
$n = 5$						0.1	
$n = 6$						−0.7	
Co^{+3}							
$n = 1$						7.3	1.3
$n = 2$						6.7	
$n = 3$						6.1	
$n = 4$						5.6	
$n = 5$						5.1	
$n = 6$						4.4	

Table 4-5 (continued)

	log K						
	F^-	Cl^-	Br^-	I^-	SCN^-	NH_3	$SO_4^{=}$
Ni^{++}							
$n = 1$	0.66				1.2	2.7	2.4
$n = 2$					0.5	2.1	
$n = 3$					0.2	1.6	
$n = 4$						1.1	
$n = 5$						0.6	
$n = 6$						−0.1	
Cu^+							
$n = 1$						5.9	
$n = 2$						4.9	
Cu^{++}							
$n = 1$	1	0	0			4.0	2.2
$n = 2$						3.3	
$n = 3$						2.7	
$n = 4$						2.0	
Ag^+							
$n = 1$	0.4					3.3	1
$n = 2$						3.9	
Zn^{++}							
$n = 1$	1.3	−0.3	−0.6	−2.9	0.5	2.2	2.3
$n = 2$		0.3	−0.4	1.3	0.4	2.3	
$n = 3$		−0.3	−0.7	−0.1		2.3	
$n = 4$		0.2	0.4	−0.6		2.0	
Cd^{++}							
$n = 1$	0.5	2.0	2.0	2.3	1.0	2.5	2.3
$n = 2$	0.1	0.7	1.3	1.6	0.7	2.0	
$n = 3$		−0.2	0.2	1	−1.0	1.3	
$n = 4$		−0.7	0.2	1	1.0	0.8	
Hg_2^{++}							
$n = 1$	<0.5						1.3
$n = 2$							1.1
Hg^{++}							
$n = 1$	1.6	6.7	8.9	12.9			1.3
$n = 2$		6.5	7.9	11.0			1.1
$n = 3$		1.0	2.3	3.7			
$n = 4$		1.0	1.8	2.4			
Al^{+3}							
$n = 1$	6.1						
$n = 2$	5.0						
$n = 3$	3.9						
$n = 4$	2.7						
$n = 5$	1.6						
$n = 6$	0.4						

Table 4-5 (continued)

	log K						
	F^-	Cl^-	Br^-	I^-	SCN^-	NH_3	$SO_4^=$
Ga^{+3}							
$n = 1$	4.5						
$n = 2$	3.5						
$n = 3$	2.5						
In^{+3}							
$n = 1$	3.8	2	1.2	2	2.6		1.8
$n = 2$	2.6		0.6	1	1.0		0.8
$n = 3$			0.7		1.0		0.4
Tl^+							
$n = 1$	0.1	0.5	0.9	0.7	0.8	−0.9	1.4
$n = 2$			0.1	0.2			
$n = 3$				0.2			
$n = 4$				−0.4			
Tl^{+3}							
$n = 1$		8.1	9.7				0.3
$n = 2$		5.5	6.9				
$n = 3$		2.2	4.6				
$n = 4$		2	2.7				
Sn^{++}							
$n = 1$	4.9	1.5	1.1				
$n = 2$		0.7	0.7				
$n = 3$		−0.2	−0.4				
$n = 4$		−0.6					
Pb^{++}							
$n = 1$	<0.8	1.1	1.8	2	0.5		
$n = 2$					0.3		

order F^-, Cl^-, Br^-, I^-. However, there are again exceptions among the later elements, particularly mercury.

Detailed explanations of trends are difficult, because in every case there is competition involved between ligand and water. Noting that the maximum difference in equilibrium constants quoted in Table 4-5 is less than 15 orders of magnitude, which corresponds to about 20 kcal per mole free-energy change, and noting that hydration free energies can exceed 1000 kcal, it is clear that we have here a problem of worrying about small differences in large numbers. The tenuous balance between ion hydration and ligand binding can be tipped by such relatively minor effects as ligand field stabilization; van der Waals attraction; multiple bonding through back donation; changes of

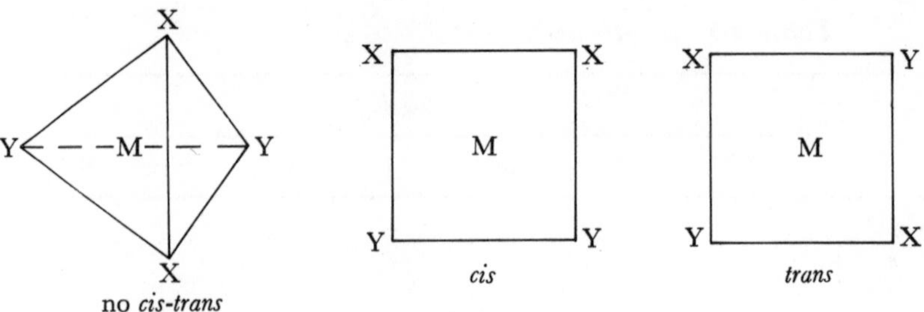

Figure 4-8 *Stereochemistry of MX_2Y_2.*

rotational, vibrational, and translational entropy on association; and even structural changes in the solvent medium.

Considering the difficulty of defining the chemical composition of complex ions in solution, one might wonder how people have the temerity to discuss stereochemistry of complexes in solution. The point is that certain elements, especially cobalt, chromium, and the platinum elements, form some complexes which undergo substitution so slowly that the complex can be transferred without change from phase to phase and so be characterized as reliably as organic structures. Just as the tetrahedral carbon atom was deduced from purely chemical studies, so the octahedral and square-planar configurations were deduced similarly. Thus, for example, the fact that $Pt(NH_3)_2Cl_2$ exists as two isomers shows that it cannot be tetrahedral but can be square-planar. Figure 4-8 shows that although each tetrahedral position is adjacent (*cis*) to every other position, this is not true for the square-planar situation. Geometrical isomerism is also possible for octahedral complexes either of the type MX_2Y_4 or MX_3Y_3. As shown in Figure 4-9, *cis* and *trans* isomers are possible in both cases.

The octahedral configurations are like the tetrahedral and unlike the square-planar in allowing optical isomerism as well as geometrical isomerism. The requirement for optical activity is the absence of a plane of symmetry and of a center of symmetry. One of the most common ways of getting an optically active octahedral species is through use of a *bidentate ligand*—that is, one which occupies two coordination sites. Examples of bidentate ligands are ethylenediamine, $NH_2CH_2CH_2NH_2$, and oxalate, $^-O_2CCO_2^-$.

The way in which bidentate ligands bring about optical isomer-

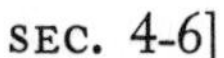

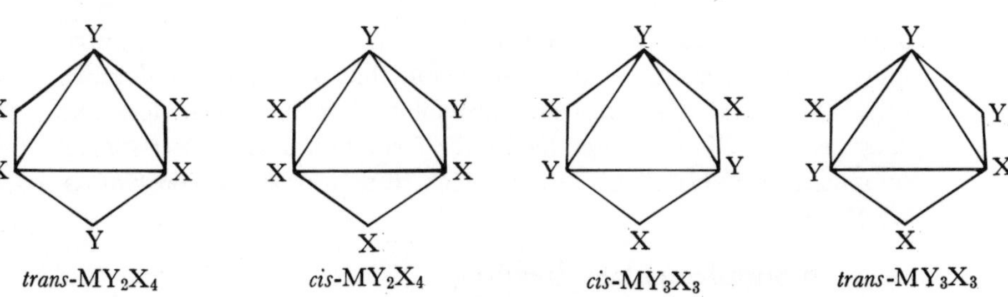

***Figure 4-9** Geometrical isomerism of octahedral complexes.*

ism is illustrated in Figure 4-10. It can be seen that one mirror image cannot be made to superimpose the other by any rotation or combination of rotations. This nonidentity arises because the species do not possess planes or centers of symmetry. The point of adding the bridging bidentate ligand groups is to destroy symmetry planes which otherwise could pass through the central metal atom and four corner positions or through the central metal atom and two *trans* positions. Of course, the existence of optical activity requires also that the chemical species remain inert to substitution long enough to permit characterization of isomers.

Through the use of substitution-inert complexes—e.g., $Co(NH_3)_6^{+3}$—considerable insight has been gained into the very basic problem of species definition. These ions are useful because the first coordination sphere is effectively blocked to substitution, so any

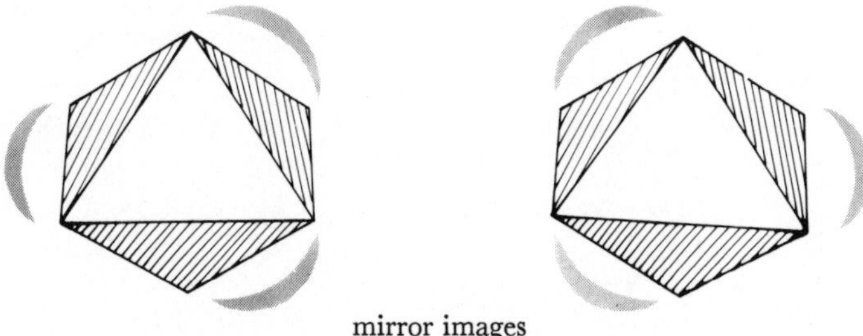

***Figure 4-10** Optical activity of octahedral complex with bidentate ligands.*

interaction between cation and anion must occur through an outer sphere. As an example, the observation that a solution containing $Pt(NH_3)_6^{+4}$ and $SO_4^{=}$ has an ultraviolet spectrum which does not obey Beer's law is accounted for by the formation of an "outer-sphere complex," $Pt(NH_3)_6SO_4^{++}$, for which the association constant is 3.3×10^3.

• Supplementary Reading

1. J. P. Hunt, "Metal Ions in Aqueous Solutions," Benjamin, New York, 1963.
2. R. A. Robinson and R. H. Stokes, "Electrolyte Solutions," 2nd ed., Butterworths, London, 1959.
3. J. Lewis and R. G. Wilkins (eds.), "Modern Coordination Chemistry," Interscience, New York, 1960.
4. W. J. Hamer (ed.), "The Structure of Electrolytic Solutions," Wiley, New York, 1959.

5

Chemical Reactions

Although thermodynamic and kinetic aspects of chemical reaction are of central importance in inorganic chemistry, these dynamic considerations too often have been made subsidiary to structure studies. The recognition of the importance of dynamic aspects and the availability of necessary tools for their study are the chief causes for the reawakening of interest in inorganic chemistry. It is to be hoped that further systematization of inorganic thermodynamic and kinetic information will lead to unifying concepts which will stimulate the field to the same extent that the tetrahedral carbon atom did to organic chemistry.

Extensive tabulations of thermodynamic properties of pure compounds are available. However, what is usually needed is this kind of information in reaction mixtures. The most common single reaction medium is the aqueous solution, so it is not surprising that the most extensive compilations of both thermodynamic and kinetic data are those for aqueous media.

• 5-1 Oxidation Potentials

The voltage $E°$ assigned to the half-reaction

$$M^{+x-n} \rightarrow M^{+x} + ne^-$$

is related to the free-energy change per electron for the half-reaction written. Thus, oxidation potentials are intensive properties as opposed to free energies, which are extensive. Their main utility is to represent systematically reaction tendencies compared to a standard. The standard is the half-reaction

$$\frac{1}{2}H_2(g) \rightarrow H^+ + e^-$$

for which the oxidation potential is set at zero for standard-state conditions (1 atm, 25°C, ideal solutions at 1 m). Thus an oxidation potential for any half-reaction strictly describes the complete reaction

$$M^{+x-n} + nH^+ \rightarrow M^{+x} + n/2H_2(g)$$

for which the standard free-energy change is $-nFE°$, where F is the Faraday (23.066 kcal per Avogadro number of electron volts).

In the event that the conditions of a reaction are not those of the standard state, the potential for the reaction can be calculated through use of the Nernst equation,

$$E = E° - \frac{RT}{nF} \ln \Pi a_i^{\nu_i}$$

where $\Pi a_i^{\nu_i}$ is the quotient of the activities of the products divided by the activities of the reactants, each raised to a power ν_i given by the numerical coefficient in the chemical equation. In practice, the activities of gases are taken as equal to their partial pressures. The activities of dissolved ions (equal to activity coefficients times concentrations—see page 3) are obtained either by use of tables of activity coefficients or calculated as by the Debye-Hückel equation.

The principal use of oxidation potentials is in deciding whether or not a given reaction is thermodynamically favored. Since the requirement for spontaneous reaction at constant temperature and pressure is a negative ΔF, this corresponds to a positive E. For the reaction

$$A + B^+ \rightarrow A^+ + B$$

a positive E means that the half-reaction $A \rightarrow A^+ + e^-$ has greater tendency to occur than the half-reaction $B \rightarrow B^+ + e^-$ and thus reverses the latter. As a corollary, given the values of oxidation potentials for a series of half-reactions, it is possible to decide the direction favored for any combination. Any half-reaction in the series can reverse any other half-reaction of lower oxidation potential. For example, given that the $E°$ for $Ti^{+3} + H_2O \rightarrow TiO^{++} + 2H^+ + e^-$ is -0.1 volt and the $E°$ for $V^{+3} + H_2O \rightarrow VO^{++} + 2H^+ + e^-$ is -0.36 volt, it follows that Ti^{+3} should reduce VO^{++} under standard-state conditions. (It should be borne in mind, however, that many reactions with unfavorable standard-state potentials can be made to occur by changing pH or other concentrations.)

Tables 5-1 and 5-2 give a list of most of the common couples (reducing agent/oxidized form) for which oxidation potentials have been assigned. Values have been selected from the extensive set given by Latimer in "Oxidation Potentials," 2nd ed., Prentice-Hall, Englewood Cliffs, N.J., 1952. They are listed in order of decreasing oxidation potential, so that any reducing agent is predicted to reduce any oxidizing agent below it in the tables.

There are two problems as to whether a particular reaction will actually occur. One is a problem of kinetics—that is, the reaction might be too slow to be observed. The other concerns the actual products of reaction in that they may not correspond to those given by the couples. To illustrate the latter point, let us focus our attention on the couples Tl^+/Tl^{+3} (-1.25 volts) and Mn^{++}/MnO_4^- (-1.51 volts). It would seem that Tl^+ should reduce MnO_4^- to give Tl^{+3} and Mn^{++}. However, on the way from MnO_4^- to Mn^{++} there is MnO_2. The potential Mn^{++}/MnO_2 is $\doteq 1.23$ volts, according to which Tl^+ cannot reduce MnO_2 further. Thus the products of the reaction are not Tl^{+3} and Mn^{++} but are instead Tl^{+3} and MnO_2. This problem of products can occur only when there are intermediate oxidation states that are stable to disproportionation.

To decide whether a particular oxidation state is stable to disproportionation—i.e., undergoes self-oxidation-reduction to give a higher and a lower oxidation state—it is convenient to display the potentials as follows:

$$Mn \xrightarrow{1.18} Mn^{++} \xrightarrow{-1.51} Mn^{+3} \xrightarrow{-0.95} MnO_2 \xrightarrow{-2.26} MnO_4^{=} \xrightarrow{-0.56} MnO_4^-$$

where the numbers give the oxidation potential of the couple formed by the adjacent species.

For the species Mn^{++} the two couples of interest are Mn/Mn^{++}

Table 5-1 Oxidation potentials in acid solution

Li/Li^{+}	3.05	Pb/PbI_2	0.37	ReO_2/ReO_4^{-}	−0.51
K/K^{+}	2.93	$Pb/PbSO_4$	0.36	$S_4O_6^{=}/H_2SO_3$	−0.51
Rb/Rb^{+}	2.93	In/In^{+3}	0.34	Cu/Cu^{+}	−0.52
Cs/Cs^{+}	2.92	Tl/Tl^{+}	0.34	Te/TeO_2	−0.53
Ra/Ra^{++}	2.92	Pt/PtS	0.30	I^{-}/I_2	−0.54
Ba/Ba^{++}	2.90	$Pb/PbBr_2$	0.28	I^{-}/I_3^{-}	−0.54
Sr/Sr^{++}	2.89	Co/Co^{++}	0.28	$CuCl/Cu^{++}$	−0.54
Ca/Ca^{++}	2.87	H_3PO_3/H_3PO_4	0.28	$Ag/AgBrO_3$	−0.55
Na/Na^{+}	2.71	$Pb/PbCl_2$	0.27	$Te/Te(OH)_3^{+}$	−0.56
La/La^{+3}	2.52	V^{++}/V^{+3}	0.26	$HAsO_2/H_3AsO_4$	−0.56
Ce/Ce^{+3}	2.48	$V/V(OH)_4^{+}$	0.25	$Ag/AgNO_2$	−0.56
Nd/Nd^{+3}	2.44	$Sn/SnF_6^{=}$	0.25	$MnO_4^{=}/MnO_4^{-}$	−0.56
Sm/Sm^{+3}	2.41	Ni/Ni^{++}	0.25	$H_2SO_3/S_2O_6^{=}$	−0.57
Gd/Gd^{+3}	2.40	$N_2H_5^{+}/N_2$	0.23	$Pt/PtBr_4^{=}$	−0.58
Mg/Mg^{++}	2.37	$S_2O_6^{=}/SO_4^{=}$	0.22	SbO^{+}/Sb_2O_5	−0.58
Y/Y^{+3}	2.37	Cu/CuI	0.19	$Pd/PdBr_4^{=}$	−0.6
Am/Am^{+3}	2.32	Ag/AgI	0.15	$Ru/RuCl_5^{=}$	−0.60
Lu/Lu^{+3}	2.25	Ge/GeO_2	0.15	U^{+4}/UO_2^{+}	−0.62
H^{-}/H_2	2.25	Sn/Sn^{++}	0.14	$Pd/PdCl_4^{=}$	−0.62
Sc/Sc^{+3}	2.08	Pb/Pb^{++}	0.13	$CuBr/Cu^{++}$	−0.64
Pu/Pu^{+3}	2.07	W/WO_3	0.09	$Au/Au(SCN)_4^{-}$	−0.66
Al/AlF_6^{-3}	2.07	$HS_2O_4^{-}/H_2SO_3$	0.08	$PtCl_4^{=}/PtCl_6^{=}$	−0.68
Th/Th^{+4}	1.90	$Hg/HgI_4^{=}$	0.04	H_2O_2/O_2	−0.68
Np/Np^{+3}	1.86	H_2/H^{+}	0.00	H_2Te/Te	−0.70
Be/Be^{++}	1.85	$Ag/Ag(S_2O_3)_2^{-3}$	−0.01	$Pt/PtCl_4^{=}$	−0.73
U/U^{+3}	1.80	$Cu/CuBr$	−0.03	Se/H_2SeO_3	−0.74
Hf/Hf^{+4}	1.70	UO_2^{+}/UO_2^{++}	−0.05	Np^{+4}/NpO_2^{+}	−0.75
Al/Al^{+3}	1.66	PH_3/P	−0.06	$Ir/IrCl_6^{-3}$	−0.77
Ti/Ti^{++}	1.63	$Ag/AgBr$	−0.10	Fe^{++}/Fe^{+3}	−0.77
Zr/Zr^{+4}	1.53	Ti^{+3}/TiO^{++}	−0.1	Hg/Hg_2^{++}	−0.79
$Si/SiF_6^{=}$	1.2	SiH_4/Si	−0.10	Ag/Ag^{+}	−0.80
$Ti/TiF_6^{=}$	1.19	$Cu/CuCl$	−0.14	N_2O_4/NO_3^{-}	−0.80
Mn/Mn^{++}	1.18	H_2S/S	−0.14	Os/OsO_4	−0.85
Ti/TiO^{++}	0.89	Np^{+3}/Np^{+4}	−0.15	CuI/Cu^{++}	−0.86
B/H_3BO_3	0.87	Sn^{++}/Sn^{+4}	−0.15	$Au/AuBr_4^{-}$	−0.87
Si/SiO_2	0.86	Sb/Sb_2O_3	−0.15	Hg_2^{++}/Hg^{++}	−0.92
Ta/Ta_2O_5	0.81	Cu^{+}/Cu^{++}	−0.15	PuO_2^{+}/PuO_2^{++}	−0.93
Zn/Zn^{++}	0.76	$Bi/BiOCl$	−0.16	HNO_2/NO_3^{-}	−0.94
Tl/TlI	0.75	$H_2SO_3/SO_4^{=}$	−0.17	NO/NO_3^{-}	−0.96
Cr/Cr^{+3}	0.74	$Hg/HgBr_4^{=}$	−0.21	$Au/AuBr_2^{-}$	−0.96
H_2Te/Te	0.72	$Ag/AgCl$	−0.22	Pu^{+3}/Pu^{+4}	−0.97
$Tl/TlBr$	0.66	$As/HAsO_2$	−0.25	$Pt/Pt(OH)_2$	−0.98
Nb/Nb_2O_5	0.65	Re/ReO_2	−0.25	Pd/Pd^{++}	−0.99
U^{+3}/U^{+4}	0.61	Bi/BiO^{+}	−0.32	$IrBr_6^{-4}/IrBr_6^{-3}$	−0.99
AsH_3/As	0.60	U^{+4}/UO_2^{++}	−0.33	NO/HNO_2	−1.00
$Tl/TlCl$	0.56	Cu/Cu^{++}	−0.34	$Au/AuCl_4^{-}$	−1.00
Ga/Ga^{+3}	0.53	$Ag/AgIO_3$	−0.35	$VO^{++}/V(OH)_4^{+}$	−1.00
SbH_3/Sb	0.51	$Fe(CN)_6^{-4}/$		$IrCl_6^{-3}/IrCl_6^{=}$	−1.02
P/H_3PO_2	0.51	$Fe(CN)_6^{-3}$	−0.36	TeO_2/H_6TeO_6	−1.02
H_3PO_2/H_3PO_3	0.50	V^{+3}/VO^{++}	−0.36	NO/N_2O_4	−1.03
Fe/Fe^{++}	0.44	Re/ReO_4^{-}	−0.36	Pu^{+4}/PuO_2^{++}	−1.04
Eu^{++}/Eu^{+3}	0.43	HCN/C_2N_2	−0.37	Br^{-}/Br_2	−1.07
Cr^{++}/Cr^{+3}	0.41	$S_2O_3^{=}/H_2SO_3$	−0.40	HNO_2/N_2O_4	−1.07
Cd/Cd^{++}	0.40	$Rh/RhCl_6^{-3}$	−0.44	$Cu(CN)_2^{-}/Cu^{++}$	−1.12
H_2Se/Se	0.40	Ag/Ag_2CrO_4	−0.45	Pu^{+4}/PuO_2^{+}	−1.15
Ti^{++}/Ti^{+3}	0.4	S/H_2SO_3	−0.45	$H_2SeO_3/SeO_4^{=}$	−1.15

Table 5-1 (*continued*)

NpO_2^+/NpO_2^{++}	−1.15	$Au/Au(OH)_3$	−1.45	$PbSO_4/PbO_2$	−1.69
ClO_3^-/ClO_4^-	−1.19	I_2/HIO	−1.45	Am^{+3}/AmO_2^{++}	−1.69
I_2/IO_3^-	−1.20	Pb^{++}/PbO_2	−1.46	MnO_2/MnO_4^-	−1.70
$HClO_2/ClO_3^-$	−1.21	Au/Au^{+3}	−1.50	Au/Au^+	−1.7
H_2O/O_2	−1.23	Mn^{++}/Mn^{+3}	−1.51	Am^{+3}/AmO_2^+	−1.73
Mn^{++}/MnO_2	−1.23	Mn^{++}/MnO_4^-	−1.51	H_2O/H_2O_2	−1.77
Tl^+/Tl^{+3}	−1.25	Br_2/BrO_3^-	−1.52	Co^{++}/Co^{+3}	−1.82
Am^{+4}/AmO_2^+	−1.26	$Br_2/HBrO$	−1.59	$Fe^{+3}/FeO_4^{=}$	−1.9
$NH_4^+/N_2H_5^+$	−1.28	BiO^+/Bi_2O_4	−1.59	Ag^+/Ag^{++}	−1.98
$HClO_2/ClO_2$	−1.28	IO_3^-/H_5IO_6	−1.6	$SO_4^{=}/S_2O_8^{=}$	−2.01
$PdCl_4^{=}/PdCl_6^{=}$	−1.29	Bk^{+3}/Bk^{+4}	−1.6	O_2/O_3	−2.07
N_2O/HNO_2	−1.29	Ce^{+3}/Ce^{+4}	−1.61	F^-/F_2O	−2.1
$Cr^{+3}/Cr_2O_7^{=}$	−1.33	$Cl_2/HClO$	−1.63	Am^{+3}/Am^{+4}	−2.18
NH_4^+/NH_3OH^+	−1.35	AmO_2^+/AmO_2^{++}	−1.64	F^-/F_2	−2.87
Cl^-/Cl_2	−1.36	$HClO/HClO_2$	−1.64	HF/F_2	−3.06
$N_2H_5^+/NH_3OH^+$	−1.42	Ni^{++}/NiO_2	−1.68		

Table 5-2 *Oxidation potentials in basic solution*

$Ca/Ca(OH)_2$	3.03	$Se^{=}/Se$	0.92	Rh/Rh_2O_3	−0.04
$Sr/Sr(OH)_2 \cdot 8H_2O$	2.99	$Sn/Sn(OH)_3^-$	0.91	$SeO_3^{=}/SeO_4^{=}$	−0.05
$Ba/Ba(OH)_2 \cdot 8H_2O$	2.97	$Sn(OH)_3^-/$		$Pd/Pd(OH)_2$	−0.07
$La/La(OH)_3$	2.90	$Sn(OH)_6^{=}$	0.90	$S_2O_3^{=}/S_4O_6^{=}$	−0.08
$Lu/Lu(OH)_3$	2.72	PH_3/P	0.89	Hg/HgO	−0.10
$Mg/Mg(OH)_2$	2.69	$Fe/Fe(OH)_2$	0.88	NH_3/N_2H_4	−0.1
$Be/Be_2O_3^{=}$	2.62	H_2/H_2O	0.83	Ir/Ir_2O_3	−0.1
$Th/Th(OH)_4$	2.48	$Cd/Cd(OH)_2$	0.81	$Co(NH_3)_6^{++}/$	
$Pu/Pu(OH)_3$	2.42	$Co/Co(OH)_2$	0.73	$Co(NH_3)_6^{+3}$	−0.1
U/UO_2	2.39	$Ni/Ni(OH)_2$	0.72	$Mn(OH)_2/$	
$Zr/ZrO_2 \cdot H_2O$	2.36	$As/As(OH)_4^-$	0.68	$Mn(OH)_3$	−0.1
$Al/Al(OH)_4^-$	2.35	$As(OH)_4^-/AsO_4^{-3}$	0.67	$Pt/Pt(OH)_2$	−0.15
$U(OH)_3/U(OH)_4$	2.2	$Sb/Sb(OH)_4^-$	0.66	$Co(OH)_2/Co(OH)_3$	−0.17
$U/U(OH)_3$	2.17	ReO_2/ReO_4^-	0.59	PbO/PbO_2	−0.25
$P/H_2PO_2^-$	2.05	Re/ReO_4^-	0.58	I^-/IO_3^-	−0.26
$B/H_2BO_3^-$	1.79	$S_2O_3^{=}/SO_3^{=}$	0.58	ClO_2^-/ClO_3^-	−0.33
$Si/SiO_3^{=}$	1.70	Re/ReO_2	0.58	Ag/Ag_2O	−0.34
$H_2PO_2^-/HPO_3^{=}$	1.57	$Te/TeO_3^{=}$	0.57	ClO_3^-/ClO_4^-	−0.36
$Mn/Mn(OH)_2$	1.55	$Fe(OH)_2/Fe(OH)_3$	0.56	$TeO_3^{=}/TeO_4^{=}$	−0.4
$Cr/Cr(OH)_3$	1.3	$Pb/Pb(OH)_3^-$	0.54	OH^-/O_2	−0.40
$Zn/Zn(CN)_4^{=}$	1.26	$S^{=}/S$	0.48	$Ni(OH)_2/NiO_2$	−0.49
$Zn/Zn(OH)_2$	1.25	Bi/Bi_2O_3	0.44	I^-/IO^-	−0.49
$Ga/Ga(OH)_4^-$	1.22	$Cu/Cu(CN)_2^-$	0.43	Ag_2O/AgO	−0.57
$Zn/Zn(OH)_4^{=}$	1.22	$Hg/Hg(CN)_4^{=}$	0.37	$MnO_2/MnO_4^{=}$	−0.60
$Cr/Cr(OH)_4^-$	1.2	$Se/SeO_3^{=}$	0.37	$RuO_4^{=}/RuO_4^-$	−0.60
$Te^{=}/Te$	1.14	Cu/Cu_2O	0.36	Br^-/BrO_3^-	−0.61
$HPO_3^{=}/PO_4^{-3}$	1.12	$Tl/TlOH$	0.34	ClO^-/ClO_2^-	−0.66
$S_2O_4^{=}/SO_3^{=}$	1.12	$Ag/Ag(CN)_2^-$	0.31	$IO_3^-/H_3IO_6^{=}$	−0.7
$W/WO_4^{=}$	1.05	$Cr(OH)_3/CrO_4^{=}$	0.13	N_2H_4/NH_2OH	−0.73
$Mo/MoO_4^{=}$	1.05	$Cu/Cu(NH_3)_2^+$	0.12	Br^-/BrO^-	−0.76
$Cd/Cd(CN)_4^{=}$	1.03	$Cu_2O/Cu(OH)_2$	0.08	OH^-/HO_2^-	−0.88
$Zn/Zn(NH_3)_4^{++}$	1.03	HO_2^-/O_2	0.08	Cl^-/ClO^-	−0.89
$In/In(OH)_3$	1.0	$Tl(OH)/Tl(OH)_3$	0.05	ClO_2^-/ClO_2	−1.16
$Pu(OH)_3/Pu(OH)_4$	0.95	$Mn(OH)_2/MnO_2$	0.05	O_2/O_3	−1.24
$SO_3^{=}/SO_4^{=}$	0.93	NO_2^-/NO_3^-	−0.01		

(1.18 volts) and Mn^{++}/Mn^{+3} (−1.51 volts). Since Mn can reduce Mn^{+3} to give Mn^{++}, it follows that Mn^{++} is stable with respect to disproportionation to Mn and Mn^{+3}. For the species Mn^{+3} the two couples are Mn^{++}/Mn^{+3} (−1.51 volts) and Mn^{+3}/MnO_2 (−0.95 volt). In this case, Mn^{++} cannot reduce MnO_2; in fact, the couple Mn^{+3}/MnO_2 is the more reducing and can reverse the couple Mn^{++}/Mn^{+3}. In other words, Mn^{+3} disproportionates. The general rule is that a species is unstable to disproportionation if the potential to the higher state is more positive than the potential from the lower state. Of course, the possibility that a particular state itself will disproportionate can invalidate conclusions concerning the stability of states adjacent to it.

Frequently, it is necessary to combine consecutive half-reactions to form a more encompassing half-reaction. In doing this, we should bear in mind that oxidation potentials are intensive properties and like temperature cannot necessarily be added meaningfully. For example, given the two half-reactions and their oxidation potentials

$$Au \rightarrow Au^{+} + e^{-} \qquad E^{\circ} = -1.7 \text{ volts}$$

$$Au^{+} \rightarrow Au^{+3} + 2e^{-} \qquad E^{\circ} = -1.4 \text{ volts}$$

the oxidation potential for the half-reaction

$$Au \rightarrow Au^{+3} + 3e^{-}$$

can be found by converting potentials, which are intensive, to free-energy changes which are extensive. For any couple, the free-energy change (in electron volts) is found by multiplying the negative of the potential by the number of electrons. Thus for the couple Au/Au^{+} the free-energy change is 1.7 ev; for the couple Au^{+}/Au^{+3}, it is (2) × (1.4), or 2.8 ev. Addition, for the couple Au/Au^{+3}, gives 4.5 ev as the free-energy change. Since oxidation potentials are negative free-energy changes per electron, the oxidation potential for the couple Au/Au^{+3} is −4.5/3, or −1.5 volts. In computing the oxidation potential for a half-reaction obtained by subtracting one half-reaction from another, it is necessary to follow the same procedure of converting to free energies before subtraction.

The line display of oxidation potentials, as given above for the manganese states, can be made more meaningful by including the oxidation potentials for couples involving only the states stable to disproportionation, viz.,

$$Mn \xrightarrow{1.18} Mn^{++} \xrightarrow{-1.51} Mn^{+3} \xrightarrow{-0.95} MnO_2 \xrightarrow{-2.26} MnO_4^{=} \xrightarrow{-0.56} MnO_4^{-}$$

$$Mn^{++} \xrightarrow{-1.23} MnO_2 \qquad MnO_2 \xrightarrow{-1.70} MnO_4^{-}$$

The Mn^{++}/MnO_2 potential is obtained by the method given above, which amounts to taking a one-to-one weighted average of the Mn^{++}/Mn^{+3} and Mn^{+3}/MnO_2 potentials. Similarly, the MnO_2/MnO_4^- potential is a two-to-one weighted average of the $MnO_2/MnO_4^=$ and $MnO_4^=/MnO_4^-$ potentials. With these added potentials, it is clear that neither Mn^{++} nor MnO_2 disproportionates to stable products. Furthermore, it is easily seen that the Tl^+/Tl^{+3} couple (-1.25 volts) can reduce MnO_4^- to MnO_2 but not MnO_2 to Mn^{++}.

As a final exercise in oxidation potentials we can consider the americium potentials

$$Am \xrightarrow{2.32} Am^{+3} \xrightarrow{-2.18} Am^{+4} \xrightarrow{-1.26} AmO_2^{+} \xrightarrow{-1.64} AmO_2^{++}$$

It is obvious that Am^{+4} is unstable to disproportionation to Am^{+3} and AmO_2^+ because the couple Am^{+4}/AmO_2^+ (-1.26 volts) is more positive than the couple Am^{+3}/Am^{+4} (-2.18 volts). It is not clear whether Am^{+3} and AmO_2^+ are stable until Am^{+4} is eliminated from consideration. The potential for the couple Am^{+3}/AmO_2^+ is -1.72 volts. Therefore, AmO_2^+ is unstable to disproportionation to Am^{+3} and AmO_2^{++}. The potential for the couple Am^{+3}/AmO_2^{++} is -1.69 volts, which indicates that Am^{+3} is stable.

It might be noted that in aqueous solution a limitation on stable species is placed by possible oxidation or reduction of the solvent. Couples more positive than 0.41 volt would be expected to liberate H_2 from pH 7 solution; couples more positive than zero, from 1 *M* H^+ solutions. Couples more negative than -0.82 volt are expected to liberate O_2 from pH 7 solution; couples more negative than -1.23 volts, from 1 *M* H^+ solutions. In all four cases, expectations are usually not fulfilled due to slow rates. However, if potentials become much more positive or much more negative than these limits, reactions with the solvent medium frequently occur.

It is easy to overlook the enormous utility of oxidation potentials as a means for summarizing a great deal of useful information. It need only be pointed out that each half-reaction added to a list of *n* half-reactions increases the number of reactions we know about by *n*.

• 5-2 Reaction Kinetics

Oxidation potentials are concerned only with the thermodynamics of reaction. They give no information about either the rate or the mechanism of the reaction. The latter subjects, in general, are part of chemical kinetics.

In general, the rate of formation of a species Z is some function of the concentration of all species present:

$$\frac{d[Z]}{dt} = \sum_i k_i[Z]^{z_i}[Y]^{y_i}[X]^{x_i} \cdots$$

The summation implies that there may be several additive terms in the rate law, in each term of which the exponents may be integral or not, positive or negative, or zero. The conclusion usually drawn from the existence of more than one term is that the reaction proceeds by more than one mechanism, depending upon the conditions. Usually it is assumed that if one of the terms is a simple product of two concentrations raised to the first power—that is, first order in Y and first order in X—the rate-limiting reaction proceeds by a collision of Y with X. If a more complicated term appears, it is usually assumed that the rate-limiting step is preceded by other steps. Because these other steps are faster, they may come to equilibrium, in which case the reverse reactions can cause inverse dependences on concentrations. Prior equilibria can also cause fractional orders.

Interpretation of experimentally determined rate laws in terms of mechanisms is difficult even for relatively simple rate laws. For one thing alternate mechanisms may lead to the same rate law. For another, the rate law may not be sufficiently complete to reveal the actual mechanism. An example of the latter concerns the possible participation of the solvent in the mechanism. Since it is usually not possible to alter the solvent concentration significantly, the dependence of rate and hence mechanism on solvent participation is completely unknown in most cases.

• 5-3 Mechanisms of Oxidation-Reduction

The traditional classification of chemical reactions as oxidation-reduction, in contrast to others such as acid-base, rests on the arbitrary assignment of oxidation state. To illustrate this arbitrary convention we can note that the formation of HI from H_2 and I_2 is called oxidation-reduction, whereas the dissociation of HI to ions in water is not; yet, the electronic balance at an H atom is at least as much changed in the latter reaction as in the former. As a consequence of this hollow definition, we can expect no unique mechanism to suffice for all oxidation-reduction reactions.

Oxidation-reduction mechanisms are usually considered in two classifications, electron transfer and atom transfer, although it is usually difficult if not impossible to distinguish the two cases experimentally. The oxidation of ferrous to ferric provides a clear illustration of the problems involved. To reduce complications to a minimum this reaction is usually studied with a radioactive tracer, which permits study of the rate of interconversion of ferrous-ferric without use of an external oxidizing or reducing agent. In a typical experiment, the radioactive tracer may be introduced in the form of ferric ion to a ferrous-ferric mixture and the rate observed at which the radioactivity appears in the ferrous species.

$$Fe^{*+3} + Fe^{++} = Fe^{*++} + Fe^{+3}$$

For these exchange experiments the most difficult experimental problem is that associated with the separation of the two oxidation states quickly and in a manner which will not itself induce exchange. Frequently employed techniques include solvent extraction, precipitation, and complex-ion formation. The rate law found experimentally for the ferrous-ferric exchange includes a number of terms and has the form

$$\text{rate} = [Fe^{++}][Fe^{+3}]\left(k_1 + \frac{k_2}{[H^+]} + k_3[A] + \cdots\right)$$

where A represents the anion present. There may be additional terms depending on higher powers of the anion concentration and on other anions that may also be present.

The existence of the several terms implies that there are several mechanisms operative. One of these, given by k_1, suggests direct reaction between the ferrous and the ferric. The one given by k_2, with its inverse dependence on H^+, has the usual significance of such terms in denoting a direct dependence on OH^-. In the ferrous-ferric case this is interpreted in terms of a prior equilibrium which forms $FeOH^{++}$, and it is this species which is thought to react with Fe^{++}. Similarly the k_3 term connotes prior formation of a ferric-anion complex such as $FeCl^{++}$, which then reacts with Fe^{++}. In chloride-containing solution the rate law can be written as

$$\text{rate} = k_1[Fe^{++}][Fe^{+3}] + k_2[Fe^{++}][FeOH^{++}] + k_3[Fe^{++}][FeCl^{++}] + k_4[Fe^{++}][FeCl_2{}^+]$$

where $k_1 = 0.87$, $k_2 = 1.0 \times 10^3$, $k_3 = 9.7$, and $k_4 = 15$, all at 0°C and in units of liter per mole per second. All these terms are small enough to show that the process is far from instantaneous.

In accounting for the slowness one usually has recourse to the Franck-Condon principle, which states that there can be no appreciable change of atomic arrangement during the time of an electronic transition. This requirement means that an electron can be transferred from a hydrated ferrous ion to a hydrated ferric ion only if vibrations within the two species have made them of identical atomic coordinate configuration. Because hydrated ferrous and hydrated ferric are substantially different species, the exact matching is fairly improbable and hence relatively long times must pass before electron transfer can occur.

Because the direct electron-transfer process is delayed, other processes can compete with it and in fact may account for most of the exchange. The additional terms in the above rate law can be interpreted as arising from formation of bridged binuclear complexes involving a ferrous and a ferric bridged by an OH, for example. The bridged complex could accelerate exchange either because it makes electron transfer more probable or because it allows exchange via atom transfer. Atom transfer can produce the same result as electron transfer, as can be seen from the following equations:

$$Fe^{*+3} + Cl^- = Fe^*Cl^{++}$$

$$Fe^*Cl^{++} + Fe^{++} = Fe^{*++} + FeCl^{++}$$

$$FeCl^{++} = Fe^{+3} + Cl^-$$

where the displacement of a neutral chlorine atom away from the radioactive ferric has reduced iron's oxidation number, and the addition of the neutral chlorine to the ferrous has oxidized iron to the ferric state.

For the hydroxide-catalyzed path the following atom-transfer scheme has been proposed:

$$Fe^{*+3} + H_2O = Fe^*OH^{++} + H^+$$

$$Fe^*OH^{++} + \begin{matrix} H \\ \diagdown \\ \quad OFe^{++} \\ \diagup \\ H \end{matrix} = \left[Fe^*O \begin{matrix} H \\ \diagup \\ \\ \diagdown \\ H \end{matrix} \right]^{++} + HOFe^{++}$$

$$HOFe^{++} + H^+ = H_2O + Fe^{+3}$$

The key step in this scheme is the second, in which a neutral hydrogen atom from a water of hydration on the ferrous is transferred to the hydrolyzed ferric ion, thereby reducing the latter to ferrous. Once the possibility of atom transfer is recognized as a way of effecting "electron transfer" it is possible to postulate atom transfer even for rate-law terms which do not involve anion dependence. For example, the k_1 term in the above rate law can be rationalized by a sequence such as follows:

$$Fe^*OH_2{}^{+3} + \begin{matrix} H \\ \diagdown \\ \quad OFe^{++} \\ \diagup \\ H \end{matrix} = Fe^*OH_3{}^{+3} + FeOH^{++}$$

$$Fe^*OH_3{}^{+3} = Fe^{*++} + H_3O^+$$

$$H_3O^+ + FeOH^{++} = Fe^{+3} + 2H_2O$$

In all these cases the formation and the dissociation of the complex species are fast and consequently little can be proved directly about their role in the mechanism. On the other hand, there are some systems involving nonlabile complexes in which the prior and the post equilibria are established slowly compared to the oxidation-reduction step. In these systems, if atoms are transferred they are trapped as a nonlabile complex and can be identified, thus giving insight into the reaction mechanism. Many such cases have been investigated, most frequently with chromic and cobaltic nonlabile complexes.

A typical result, for a case analogous to the ferrous-ferric system, is that found for the reaction between $CrCl^{++}$ and labeled chromous, Cr^{*++}. In the reaction it is found that none of the radioactivity originally in the chromous appears in the species $Cr(H_2O)_6{}^{+3}$. The reaction has gone completely, as given by the equation

$$CrCl^{++} + Cr^{*++} = Cr^{++} + ClCr^{*++}$$

In other words, a chlorine atom is transferred each time a chromous is oxidized. This result provides strong evidence in support of chlorine-bridging of the chromous and chromic forms in the activated complex. However, it does not prove that the oxidation mechanism is one of atom transfer, since it is equally valid to postulate that an electron has passed from chromous to chromic through an intervening chlor*ide* followed by a transfer of chlor*ide* in the opposite direction.

A large number of oxidation-reduction reactions correspond to a two-unit change in oxidation state. In the light of the Franck-Condon principle these would seem to be quite improbable as direct electron-transfer reactions because, with a two-unit difference of oxidation number, identity of reacting states is harder to achieve. Therefore, atom transfer is the more likely process, even more so than for the one-electron case. Direct experiments with O^{18} transfer substantiate this assumption for the case of sulfite reduction of $ClO_3{}^-$ to ClO^- and $BrO_3{}^-$ to BrO^-.

$$\begin{matrix} O^= \\ O\,S \\ O \end{matrix} + \left[\begin{matrix} & O^{18} \\ O^{18}Cl & \\ & O^{18} \end{matrix}\right]^- = \left[\begin{matrix} O \\ O\,S\,O^{18} \\ O \end{matrix}\right]^= + \left[\begin{matrix} & O^{18} \\ Cl & \\ & O^{18} \end{matrix}\right]^-$$

$$\begin{matrix} O^= \\ O\,S \\ O \end{matrix} + \left[\begin{matrix} & O^{18} \\ O^{18}Cl & \\ & \end{matrix}\right]^- = \left[\begin{matrix} O \\ O\,S\,O^{18} \\ O \end{matrix}\right]^= + [ClO^{18}]^-$$

Much more complicated examples of oxidation-reduction are afforded by oxidations which involve either O_2 or H_2O_2. A source of complexity here is the oxygen-to-oxygen bond which must be formed or destroyed. As a general rule, the O-to-O bond is maintained throughout as much of the reaction as possible. Thus, if O_2 or H_2O_2 act as oxidizing agents, most of the actual oxidation occurs before the O—O bond is broken.

Perhaps surprising but consistent with this behavior is the observation made for the reaction between labeled H_2O_2 and $SO_3^{=}$. In the product $SO_4^{=}$, two of the four oxygens are derived from the H_2O_2. The suggestion is that a peroxy-sulfite species is formed as an intermediate, thus preserving the O—O bond until a final rearrangement to sulfate occurs. A possible sequence is

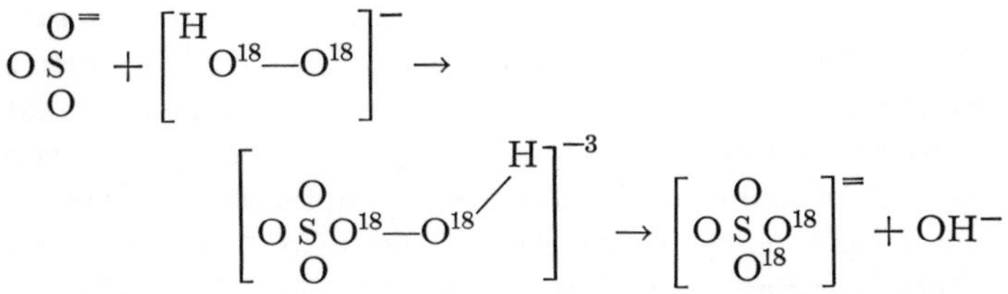

$$\begin{array}{c} O^{=} \\ O\,S \\ O \end{array} + \left[\begin{array}{l} H \\ \quad O^{18}\text{—}O^{18} \\ \end{array}\right]^{-} \rightarrow$$

$$\left[\begin{array}{l} \qquad\qquad\qquad\quad H \\ \;\;O \qquad\qquad\;\; / \\ O\,S\,O^{18}\text{—}O^{18} \\ \;\;O \end{array}\right]^{-3} \rightarrow \left[\begin{array}{c} O \\ O\,S\,O^{18} \\ O^{18} \end{array}\right]^{=} + OH^{-}$$

Another example of the preservation of the O—O bond lies in the general observations on molecular oxygen oxidations in solution. Almost invariably these seem to go by way of peroxy intermediates; as a consequence, oxygen is not so powerful an oxidizing agent as the potential -1.23 volts for the couple H_2O/O_2 would indicate. Instead the pertinent potential is -0.67 volt, which is the value for the couple H_2O_2/O_2. Further consideration of oxygen and peroxide reactions runs into considerable trouble because of inadequate experimental criteria for judging mechanisms. In addition to the above, these may also include chain mechanisms involving various free radicals.

• 5-4 Mechanisms of Substitution

Inherently simpler to interpret than oxidation-reduction reactions are substitution reactions of complex ions in which one ligand is replaced by another. The reason why many of these substitutions are easier to figure out than most oxidation-reductions is that a greater fraction of the structure is retained throughout the reaction. In this respect, these reactions resemble those involving organic compounds. However, there are at least two major points of difference between organic and inorganic substitutions.

In the first place, a variety of central atoms can be used, thus allowing study of the influence of the central atom's electron configuration on the course of the reaction. Second, whereas organic substitutions are limited to tetrahedral or lower coordination geometry, inorganic systems can also have the complications associated with square-planar or octahedral coordination. These complications arise because of the greater number of coordinate positions for the octahedron and because the positions, for both the octahedron and the square-planar case, are not all mutually adjacent as they are in a tetrahedron.

We have already mentioned previously that complexes differ drastically in their rates of substitution and in fact are frequently classified as *labile* (quick to substitute) and *nonlabile* (slow to substitute). H. Taube has pointed out that for octahedral complexes there is a correlation between lability and electron configuration in that metal atoms having three and only three *d* orbitals (the t_{2g} set) occupied are especially slow in substitution. As examples, we can cite any Cr^{+3} complex (d^3 configuration), the Fe^{++} and Co^{+3} complexes of low spin (d^6 configuration), as well as low-spin Fe^{+3} complexes (d^5).

In accounting for the correlation Taube stressed the importance of the energy difference between the ground state of the complex and the activated intermediate in the substitution reaction. Using the valence-bond language, the nonlabile complexes are those in which three *d* orbitals are occupied by nonbonding electrons. Two *d* orbitals are hybridized along with an *s* and three *p*'s to give an octahedral set for binding six ligands. Because all the *d* orbitals are used up, none is available for accommodating an incoming substituent. Any other electronic configuration leaves available at least one *d* orbital of energy comparable to one of the *d*'s used in hybrid bond formation. This empty *d* orbital can bind an added ligand, the reaction then being completed by expulsion of a different ligand. Activation-energy differences between different central metal atoms are associated with differences in availability of the orbital used to bind the seventh ligand.

The explanation just given for complex-ion lability has been criticized as being too restrictive, requiring as it does that all labile complex-ion substitutions proceed via a coordination-number-seven intermediate. There is a ligand field explanation which avoids this restriction. It ascribes activation-energy differences between various central metal ions to differences in loss of ligand field stabilization energy on going from sixfold coordination to either sevenfold (pentagonal bipyramid) or fivefold (square pyramid) coordination. The greatest loss of stabilization energy occurs for atoms having the three orbitals of the t_{2g} set occupied (either singly or doubly) and having no electrons in the upper set, e_g. In addition there is one other configuration that belongs to this category—high-spin d^8, which is energetically equivalent to d^3. With the exception of d^8, these are exactly the complexes which are slow to substitute. The case of the d^8 complexes should provide a test between the alternate theories, since the valence-bond approach predicts fast substitution while the ligand field approach predicts slow substitution. Unfortunately there is disagreement concerning lability classification of experimental data for octahedral d^8 complexes.

In the above discussion it is mentioned that ligand substitution can go through an intermediate state in which the coordination shell either is decreased to five or expanded to seven. In the former case, the octahedral complex must dissociate prior to taking on the new substituent. Since this can proceed by a unimolecular reaction, the mechanism is often designated S_N1 (substitution, nucleophilic, first order). In the latter case, the octahedral complex must add the new substituent as a seventh group prior to expulsion of one of the others. Since this addition can proceed by a bimolecular reaction, the mechanism is designated S_N2.

Both of these mechanisms are but limiting cases of a general substitution which can be represented as follows:

$$Y + MX_6 \rightarrow Y \cdots MX_5 \cdots X \rightarrow YMX_5 + X$$

In the one limiting case (S_N1), the M—X bond would have broken completely before the M—Y bond formed; the rate of substitution would then be independent of the concentration of Y. In the other limiting case (S_N2), the M—Y bond would have formed before the M—X bond started to break; the rate of substitution would then depend directly on the concentration of Y. Obviously, it is difficult to isolate the bond-making from the bond-breaking steps both in principle and in experiment. One major source of difficulty in interpreting the experiments comes from the possible participation of the solvent. Thus a rate independent cf Y could denote either S_N1 substitution or S_N2 with participation of the solvent as opposed to Y.

Because it is so difficult to get significant information on substitution mechanisms from kinetic studies, considerable work has been done on the stereochemical analysis of the products formed in the substitution reactions. The purpose of such experiments is to decide whether the entering ligand occupies the same position formerly occupied by the leaving group ("direct attack") or whether the entering ligand takes up a position *cis* to the site of the leaving group ("edge displacement") or *trans* to the site of the leaving group ("*trans* elimination"). For stereochemical analysis it is necessary that the reactant and product be "marked" either as to *cis-trans* or optical isomerism. In the discussion that follows we restrict ourselves to *cis-trans* examples since these are easier to visualize, but the same principles apply to substitution reactions involving *d* or *l* isomers.

The kind of experiments that have been performed have started with a pure isomer, allowed it to substitute, and checked the product to see whether the original configuration has been preserved or altered. As will be seen, such experiments by themselves do not allow a decision between S_N1 and S_N2 mechanisms but they may give information concerning proximity of entering and leaving groups.

If substitution occurs by a S_N1 mechanism, dissociation must occur first. For the case where MX_4AB reacts with Y to give MX_4AY and B, this means

$$MX_4AB \rightarrow MX_4A + B$$

If the configuration of the MX_4A grouping remains the same in the intermediate as it was in the initial complex MX_4AB, then incoming group Y can only take up the position vacated by B. As a result, the relative placing (*cis* or *trans*) of Y with respect to A is the same as was that of B. In other words, configuration is retained; a *cis* product results from a *cis* reactant, or a *trans* product, from a *trans* reactant.

On the other hand, if the configuration of the MX_4A grouping rearranges, as to give a more symmetrical intermediate, then the addition of Y may occur at any position, thus leading to *cis* or *trans* products. The relative amount of *cis* and *trans* products depends on several factors, including the geometry of the intermediate and the point at which Y enters. One possible intermediate geometry, trigonal bipyramid with A in the equatorial plane, and two alternatives for Y attack are shown in Figure 5-1. Assuming that Y attack is limited to the edges of the equatorial plane and ignoring selective interactions between Y and the other ligands, in the case shown it would seem that a *cis*-substituted product is twice as probable as a *trans*. However, we hasten to note that due to ligand-ligand repulsion, attack is more probable on the face than on the edge and extensive rearrangement is subsequently needed to form the octahedral product. The course of this rearrangement would determine the geometry of the product.

If substitution occurs by a S_N2 mechanism, the first step would be addition of Y to MX_4AB to give MX_4ABY. B then leaves and re-

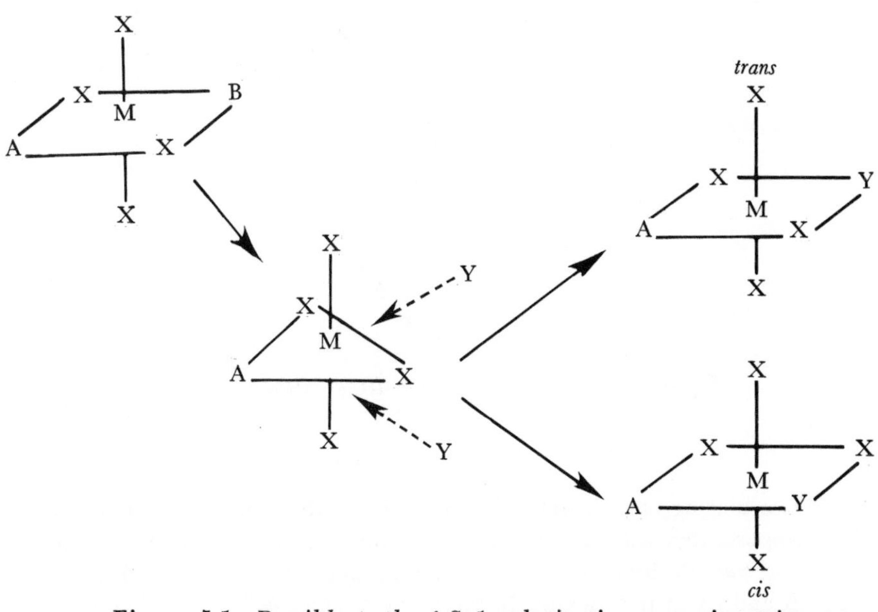

Figure 5-1 *Possible path of S_N1 substitution assuming trigonal bipyramid intermediate.*

arrangement to final product occurs. The geometry of the product is determined by the geometry of the seven-coordinate intermediate and the mode of the rearrangement. Because these have not been experimentally separated, it is customary to combine them in the discussion of the over-all process and consider the combination not in terms of mechanism, but schematically as "direct attack," "edge displacement," or "*trans* elimination."

"Direct attack" can be visualized as a process, illustrated in Figure 5-2, in which Y approaches the center of a face adjacent to B, and, as B leaves, Y takes its place. Clearly, configuration is retained, so that *cis*-MX_4AB converts to *cis*-MX_4AY and *trans*-MX_4AB converts to *trans*-MX_4AY.

"Edge displacement" is more complicated. As shown in Figure 5-3, it involves, after formation of the seven-coordinate intermediate, a simultaneous shift of three ligands—viz., the substituting Y, the X which moves out of Y's way toward B, and the B which is thereby expelled. The configuration of the final product depends on the rela-

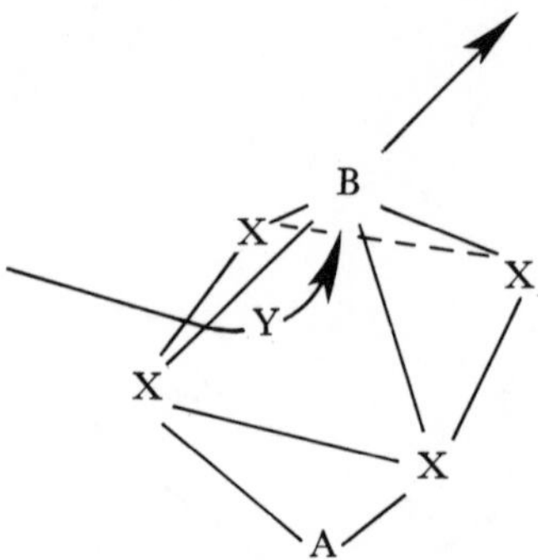

Figure 5-2 *Substitution by direct attack.*

tive placing of A in the initial complex with respect to B and, more importantly, with respect to the X ligand that moves. If A is *cis* to B and *trans* to the moving X, the final product will be *trans;* if A is *cis* to B and *cis* to the moving X, the final product will be *cis*. Thus, *cis*-MX_4AB can give either *cis*-MX_4AY or *trans*-MX_4AY. If A is *trans* to B, it must be *cis* to the moving X and the product must be *cis*, so on substitution by edge displacement *trans*-MX_4AB goes over to *cis*-MX_4AY.

"*Trans* elimination" would seem to be quite different from "edge displacement," as suggested by Figure 5-4, where Y substitutes

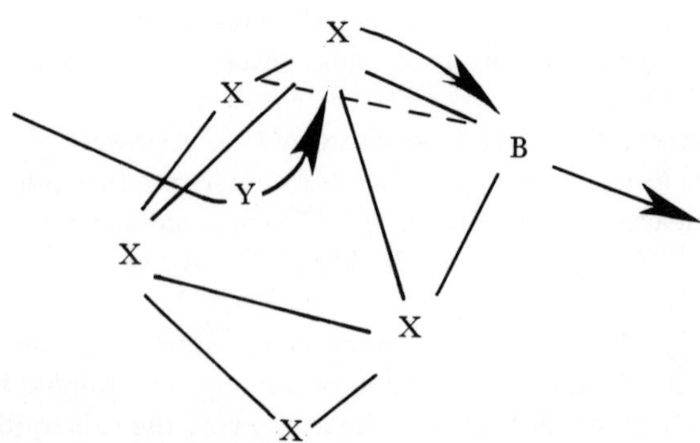

Figure 5-3 *Substitution by edge displacement.*

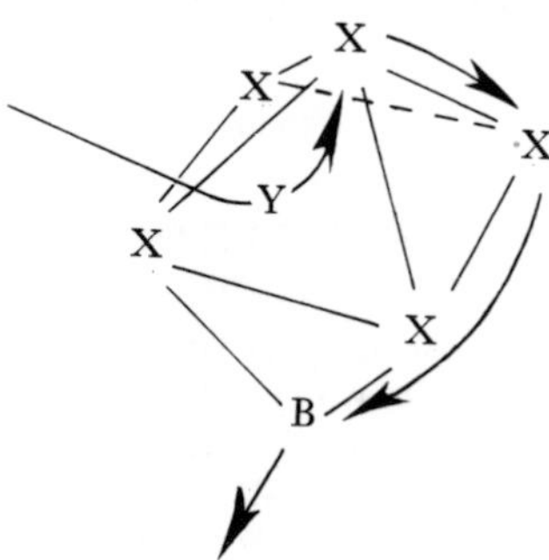

Figure 5-4 *Substitution by trans elimination.*

trans to the site vacated by B. However, it turns out that for any "*trans* elimination" it is possible to find a single "edge displacement" which leads to the same product. Thus the distribution of products that was noted above for the result of "edge displacement" mechanism is the same as that produced by any other rearrangement mechanism. It is interesting to note that the well-known Walden inversion for tetrahedral species can be viewed as an edge displacement.

Table 5-3 summarizes the predicted products for each mechanism discussed. As can be seen, there is no way product analysis can be used to decide between S_N1 and S_N2 mechanisms. However, if configuration is not retained during reaction, it is possible to eliminate "no rearrangement S_N1" and "direct attack S_N2." If a *trans* isomer goes over to a *trans* product, then "edge displacement" can be eliminated.

Table 5-3 *Products of substitution reactions*

	S_N1		S_N2	
Reactant	No rearrangement	With rearrangement	Direct attack	Edge displacement
trans	*trans*	*cis* and/or *trans*	*trans*	*cis*
cis	*cis*	*cis* and/or *trans*	*cis*	*cis* and/or *trans*

Table 5-4 *Distribution of substituted isomers*

Reactant	Product	% *cis*	% *trans*
cis-$Coen_2(NH_3)Cl^{++}$	$Coen_2(NH_3)(H_2O)^{+3}$	75	25
trans-$Coen_2(NH_3)Cl^{++}$	$Coen_2(NH_3)(H_2O)^{+3}$	20	80
cis-$Coen_2(NO_2)Cl^{+}$	$Coen_2(NO_2)(H_2O)^{++}$	100	0
trans-$Coen_2(NO_2)Cl^{+}$	$Coen_2(NO_2)(H_2O)^{++}$	0	100
cis-$Coen_2(NH_3)Cl^{++}$	$Coen_2(NH_3)OH^{++}$	84	16
trans-$Coen_2(NH_3)Cl^{++}$	$Coen_2(NH_3)OH^{++}$	76	24
cis-$Coen_2(NO_2)Cl^{+}$	$Coen_2(NO_2)OH^{+}$	66	34
trans-$Coen_2(NO_2)Cl^{+}$	$Coen_2(NO_2)OH^{+}$	6	94
cis-$Coen_2(SCN)Cl^{+}$	$Coen_2(SCN)OH^{+}$	82	18
trans-$Coen_2(SCN)Cl^{+}$	$Coen_2(SCN)OH^{+}$	76	24
cis-$Coen_2(NH_3)(H_2O)^{+3}$	$Coen_2(NH_3)(NO_2)^{++}$	80	20
trans-$Coen_2(NH_3)(H_2O)^{+3}$	$Coen_2(NH_3)(NO_2)^{++}$	35	65
cis-$Coen_2(NO_2)(H_2O)^{++}$	$Coen_2(NO_2)_2^{+}$	100	0
trans-$Coen_2(NO_2)(H_2O)^{++}$	$Coen_2(NO_2)_2^{+}$	0	100
cis-$Coen_2(NO_2)(H_2O)^{++}$	$Coen_2(NO_2)SCN^{+}$	100	0
trans-$Coen_2(NO_2)(H_2O)^{++}$	$Coen_2(NO_2)SCN^{+}$	0	100

Table 5-4 gives some indication of the results that have been observed on the distribution of products from substituting one ligand for another in some cobalt(III) bis-ethylenediamine complexes $Coen_2XY$. Values are taken from "Mechanisms of Inorganic Reactions" by F. Basolo and R. G. Pearson (Wiley, New York, 1958). Predominantly, there is retention of configuration, but in some cases there are mixed products and in two of these inversion predominates. The conclusion is that, in at least some cases, a mechanism involving some sort of rearrangement must occur. Further, there are several examples in which all or part of a *trans* reactant is converted to a *trans* product. In these cases, the *trans*-to-*trans* reaction cannot occur by edge displacement.

As a concluding note to this section, we might point out that the discussion has been confined exclusively to substitutions on octahedral complexes. One of the reasons for this is that these are the most numerous in inorganic chemistry. In fact, there are no tetrahedral metal complexes sufficiently nonlabile to permit mechanistic studies. So far as square-planar complexes are concerned, it seems probable that in solution these represent octahedra of various degrees of distortion. In regard to the so-called planar complexes of Pt(II) there is an interesting phenomenon known as the "*trans*" effect. This refers to the labilization of ligands produced by groups *trans* to them.

To illustrate we consider the substitution of Y for X in the complex PtX_2AB.

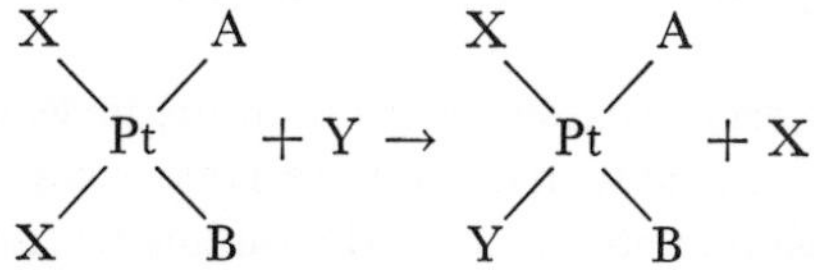

Y could have substituted *trans* to either A or B. The fact that it has substituted *trans* to A leads to the designation of bigger "*trans* effect" for A than for B. The magnitude of the *trans*-directing influence increases in the order represented by the following series:

$$H_2O < OH^- < NH_3 < \text{pyridine} < Cl^- < Br^- < SCN^- \approx I^- \approx NO_2^- \approx SO_3H^- \approx PR_3 < NO < CO \approx C_2H_4 \approx CN^-$$

It has been noted that the *trans*-directing ability increases in the order of increasing ability to form metal-ligand π bonds and also in the order of increasing polarizability of the ligand. Both of these could have the effect of piling up negative charge in the region of the *trans*-directing ligand at the expense of electron density at the opposite side. This would both weaken the bond to the ligand in the *trans* position and, furthermore, minimize repulsion for the entering *trans* substituent. Whatever the kinetic cause, differences in the "*trans* effect" can be used to control the relative placing of ligands so as to produce desired isomers at will. For example, because ethylene is more *trans*-directing than chlorine, which in turn is more so than is ammonia, different isomers can be prepared by changing the order of substitution, as follows:

$$PtCl_4^{=} \xrightarrow{C_2H_4} PtCl_3(C_2H_4)^- \xrightarrow{NH_3} trans\text{-}PtCl_2(NH_3)C_2H_4$$

$$PtCl_4^{=} \xrightarrow{NH_3} PtCl_3(NH_3)^- \xrightarrow{C_2H_4} cis\text{-}PtCl_2(NH_3)C_2H_4$$

• 5-5 Acid-Base Reactions

In the broad sense the substitution reactions just discussed are acid-base reactions because metal ions are Lewis acids and ligands are Lewis bases. However, structurally and kinetically there is little resemblance between complex-ion substitutions and what are conventionally included in the acid-base classification. The latter are among the fastest of all chemical reactions. Yet, modern techniques, particularly as employed by M. Eigen, yield valuable insight into the intriguing field of these reactions.

One of the most powerful techniques has been the investigation of relaxation phenomena associated with the application of sound waves or electric pulses, etc., to solution equilibria. Measurements consist of determination of phase lag or decay time associated with return to equilibrium. For example, if there is a large instantaneous increase in the electric field on a solution containing a partly dissociated electrolyte, there will be an increase of conductivity with time. If the field is quickly decreased the conductivity drops with finite decay time. By comparing the time lag in the conductivity changes with that found for a strong electrolyte, it is possible to assess the rates at which association and dissociation occur. Indicative of the results obtained by Eigen's use of techniques of this type are his values as given in Table 5-5.

The proton addition reactions given in the table are all of the order of 10^{11} liters per mole per second, which corresponds to extremely fast reaction and in fact is of the magnitude expected for simple collision of two oppositely charged ions in solution. Proton transfer from species shown in the table other than water are in general one to two orders of magnitude slower. Much of the difference has to do with the

Table 5-5 *Specific rate constants at 20°C (in liters per mole per second)*

Reaction	$k_{forward}$
$H^+ + OH^- \rightarrow H_2O$	1.3×10^{11}
$H^+ + F^- \rightarrow HF$	1.0×10^{11}
$H^+ + SH^- \rightarrow H_2S$	7.5×10^{10}
$H^+ + SO_4^= \rightarrow HSO_4^-$	ca. 1×10^{11}
$H^+ + CH_3COO^- \rightarrow CH_3COOH$	4.7×10^{10}
$OH^- + NH_4^+ \rightarrow NH_3 + H_2O$	3.4×10^{10}
$OH^- + HCO_3^- \rightarrow CO_3^= + H_2O$	ca. 6×10^9
$OH^- + HCrO_4^- \rightarrow CrO_4^= + H_2O$	ca. 6×10^9
$OH^- + HPO_4^= \rightarrow PO_4^{-3} + H_2O$	ca. 2×10^9
$OH^- + HP_2O_7^{-3} \rightarrow P_2O_7^{-4} + H_2O$	4.7×10^8

enhanced mobility of H_3O^+ relative to the other proton donors. Minor individual differences have been ascribed to differences of charge, configuration, detailed electronic states of donors and acceptors, and hydrogen bonding.

An important dividend from studies of fast reactions in solution has been the elucidation of the state of the actual species in such systems as aqueous CO_2 and SO_2. It has been long known that some of the equilibria in aqueous CO_2 are not rapidly established (e.g., fading of "end point" after first addition of base to CO_2 solution). However, it remained for fast-reaction techniques to unravel the several reactions. For the scheme

$$\begin{array}{ccc} & H^+ + HCO_3^- & \\ {}^{k_1}\nearrow\!\!\swarrow{}_{k_1'} & & {}_{k_2'}\nwarrow\!\!\searrow{}^{k_2} \\ CO_2 + H_2O & \underset{k_3'}{\overset{k_3}{\rightleftharpoons}} & H_2CO_3 \end{array}$$

the values of the specific rate constants are given in Table 5-6 together with the corresponding constants for the aqueous SO_2 system.

It might be noted that the true dissociation constant for carbonic acid, equal to k_2'/k_2, is equal to 1.7×10^{-4}, in contrast to the usually given value 4×10^{-7}, which assumes all of the CO_2 is as H_2CO_3. The large difference between the two dissociation constants is a consequence of the fact that practically none of the CO_2 is as H_2CO_3. The ratio of H_2CO_3 to CO_2 is given by k_3/k_3', which is 3×10^{-3}. In contrast, for SO_2 solutions an appreciable fraction is as H_2SO_3, the ratio of H_2SO_3

Table 5-6 *Specific rate constants for CO_2 and SO_2 systems*

	CO_2(25°C)	SO_2(20°C)
$XO_2 + H_2O \underset{k_1'}{\overset{k_1}{\rightleftharpoons}} H^+ + HXO_3^-$	$k_1 = 4.3 \times 10^{-2}$ sec^{-1} $k_1' = 5.6 \times 10^4\ M^{-1}$/sec	3.4×10^6 sec^{-1} $2 \times 10^8\ M^{-1}$/sec
$H^+ + HXO_3^- \underset{k'}{\overset{k_2}{\rightleftharpoons}} H_2XO_3$	$k_2 = 4.7 \times 10^{10}\ M^{-1}$/sec $k_2' = 8 \times 10^6$ sec^{-1}	$>10^{10}\ M^{-1}$/sec $>10^9$ sec^{-1}
$XO_2 + H_2O \underset{k_3'}{\overset{k_3}{\rightleftharpoons}} H_2XO_3$	$k_3 = 4.3 \times 10^{-2}$ sec^{-1} $k_3' = 15$ sec^{-1}	3.4×10^6 sec^{-1} 6.3×10^7 sec^{-1}

to SO_2 being 5×10^{-2}. It is interesting to note that for both the case of CO_2 and for the case of SO_2, $k_1 = k_3$. The reason for this identity is that both reactions, 1 and 3, involve the same reactants, giving, however, different products. The implication is that the same slow process limits both reactions; it is probable that it entails the rearrangement of the XO_2 molecule in the activated complex. The existence of the inequalities, $k_1' \neq k_2$ and $k_2' \neq k_3'$, despite their involving identical reactants in each case, indicates the influence on rates of the relative difficulty of XO_2 formation.

• 5-6 Ion Pairing

The same techniques of fast-reaction kinetics that are so informative for acid-base reactions are likewise applicable to the problem of association of ions other than H^+ or OH^- in solution. An interesting example is given by the reaction of sulfate with various metal ions. On the basis of Coulombic attraction we might expect these associations to occur more rapidly than the previously discussed protonations, which have specific rate constants of the order of 10^{11} liters per mole per sec. However, as can be seen from the Eigen values in Table 5-7, for the cases quoted the ion association rates are considerably slower than expected for diffusion-controlled reactions. It is probable that the rate-determining process in these ion associations is the elimination of water from between the metal and anion. Borrowing the picturesque language of organic chemists, we can describe the slow process as a rearrangement of a "solvent-separated ion pair" to an "intimate ion pair."

One possible scheme for the reactions is as follows:

$$(1)\quad M(H_2O)_n{}^{++} + SO_4(H_2O)_m{}^{=} \rightarrow M(H_2O)_n{}^{++}\cdot SO_4(H_2O)_m{}^{=}$$

$$(2)\quad M(H_2O)_n{}^{++}\cdot SO_4(H_2O)_m{}^{=} \rightarrow (H_2O)_{n-1}^{++}M(H_2O)SO_4{}^{=}(H_2O)_{m-1} + H_2O$$

$$(3)\quad (H_2O)_{n-1}^{++}M(H_2O)SO_4{}^{=}(H_2O)_{m-1} \rightarrow (H_2O)_{n-1}^{++}M\ SO_4{}^{=}(H_2O)_{m-1} + H_2O$$

The first step merely involves the diffusion together of two hydrated ions. It is a rearrangement of the ionic atmosphere and is thought to

Table 5-7 Ion association rate constants at 20°C (in sec^{-1})

Reactants		k_{assoc}	k_{dissoc}
Be^{++}	$SO_4^{=}$	1×10^2	1×10^3
Mg^{++}	$SO_4^{=}$	1×10^5	8×10^5
Mg^{++}	$S_2O_3^{=}$	1×10^5	1.3×10^6
Mg^{++}	$CrO_4^{=}$	1×10^5	
Ca^{++}	$CrO_4^{=}$	2×10^7	1.5×10^8
Mn^{++}	$SO_4^{=}$	4×10^6	1.5×10^7
Fe^{++}	$SO_4^{=}$	1×10^6	1×10^7
Co^{++}	$SO_4^{=}$	2×10^5	2.5×10^6
Ni^{++}	$SO_4^{=}$	1×10^4	1×10^5
Cu^{++}	$SO_4^{=}$	$>1 \times 10^7$	1.1×10^8
Zn^{++}	$SO_4^{=}$	$>1 \times 10^7$	1.9×10^8
Fe^{+3}	$SO_4^{=}$	5×10^2	10
Al^{+3}	$SO_4^{=}$	1	4

be very fast. Step (2) involves stripping at least one water off the anion so that the anion and cation are separated by a single water molecule in what is called an "outer-sphere complex." It is believed that step (2) is somewhat slower than step (1) but still quite fast (of the order of 10^9 moles per liter per sec or faster). Finally, step (3) occurs so as to eliminate at least one water molecule from between the pair of ions to form the intimate ion pair.

It is thought that the last water eliminated is one previously bound to the cation and so the rate constants quoted in Table 5-6, which refer to this slowest step, measure the rate of substitution of anion into the primary hydration sphere of the cation. That the rate constants (k_{assoc}) do indeed apply to loss of the cation hydration is supported by the observation that for the case of Mg^{++} the k's are independent of the anion. It might be noted, however, that this independence of anion is not always found. For example, in the case of ferric ion the rate of substitution increases by approximately three orders of magnitude in the series $Br^- < Cl^- < SCN^- < SO_4^{=} < F^-$, an observation which does not necessarily negate the assumption that reaction is limited by loss of cation hydration but may simply indicate that the anion assists in water removal.

Examination of the association rates given in Table 5-6 discloses a primary dependence upon cation charge: +3 ions substitute more slowly than +2. Furthermore, there seems to be a dependence on radius: in the series Be^{++}, Mg^{++}, Ca^{++} the smaller the ion the slower the substitution. Both of these influences, higher charge and smaller radius, are consistent with tighter binding of the hydration water to the cation. For the +2 transition metal ions, where the radii are quite similar to the radius of Mg^{++}, the rates are in general a bit faster than expected. The decrease observed for the series $Mn^{++} > Fe^{++} > Co^{++} > Ni^{++}$ correlates nicely with increasing ligand field stabilization of the hydrated ion. The extra-rapid rates for Cu^{++} and Zn^{++} may be the consequences of different geometries—i.e., distorted octahedron and tetrahedron, respectively.

Examination of the dissociation rates given in Table 5-6 discloses that there is the same decreasing trend for k_{dissoc} with decreasing size, increasing charge, and increasing crystal field stabilization as there is for k_{assoc}. Because there is this parallel trend the ratio of the two rate constants, $k_{\text{assoc}}/k_{\text{dissoc}}$, is about 0.1 in every case. This value is the equilibrium constant for inner-sphere ion-pair formation from the solvent-separated ion pair. It should be noted that most static measurements of complex-ion formation constants do not distinguish between the inner-sphere and the outer-sphere complexes. For example, d-c conductivity is decreased by any kind of pairing, so that constants so found would be expected to be an order of magnitude larger than those found by direct methods such as spectrophotometry, Raman spectroscopy, or relaxation measurement.

• 5-7 Interphase Reactions

The preceding sections have dealt with homogeneous or solution reactions. We briefly turn now to the more complicated case of reactions which involve more than one phase. An important example and one that has received considerable study is the case of "corrosion" or "tarnishing" reactions. The simplest of these involves reaction of a metal M with a gas X to produce a single solid product MX. As reaction proceeds starting with fresh metal, a film of MX builds up on the surface. The rate can be followed by measuring film thickness, as by determination of the increase in weight per unit area of original surface as a function of time. Ordinarily, the results fall into one of three rate-law categories as illustrated in Figure 5-5.

Linear law. In this case, the rate of film growth is constant with

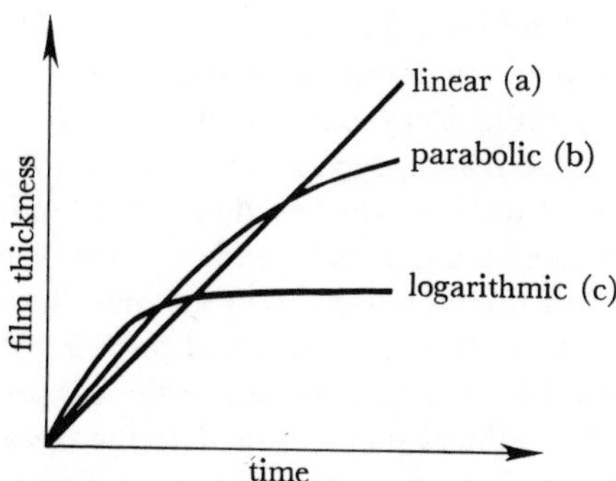

Figure 5-5 *Tarnishing reactions.*

time. In other words, film thickness α is directly proportional to time of growth,

$$\alpha = kt$$

This behavior is characteristic of the oxidation of group I and group II elements, exclusive of Be. It is associated with a reaction which produces a volume decrease, in that the volume occupied per gram-atom of metal M is less in the MX film than it is in the pure metal phase.

Parabolic law. In this case, the rate of film growth decreases with time, and the film thickness is given by the relation

$$\alpha = kt^{1/2}$$

This is the most common behavior and is shown by Be and many of the transition elements (e.g., oxidation of beryllium; reaction of Ag with halogens or sulfur; oxidation of Cu, Ni, Ti, Zr).

Logarithmic law. In this case, the rate of film growth is relatively rapid at the start but then decreases markedly with time. The film thickness as a function of time can be written

$$\alpha = k_1 \ln (k_2 t)$$

This more complicated dependence has been used to describe the oxidation of aluminum and chromium.

In interpreting these rate behaviors it can be assumed that the reaction occurs in three stages: (1) adsorption of the gas on the metal,

(2) formation of a thin film, (3) growth of the film. The type of kinetics observed depends on the nature of the limiting step. In considering the three possible limiting steps, only the third should depend on film thickness. If for some reason, such as cracking and flaking off of the film as a result of contraction, the reaction is not limited by step (3), then the corrosion rate should be independent of the extent of corrosion —hence, a linear law should obtain. On the other hand, if step (3) is limiting, the process needs to be considered further. After formation of an initial film, reaction can proceed only if there is transport through the film either of M to the X phase or of X to the metal phase.

For the case of silver and sulfur, there is a classic experiment by C. Wagner, in which he determined that the weight of one Ag_2S wafer next to the sulfur phase increased, whereas the weight of an adjacent Ag_2S wafer next to the silver phase did not. The interpretation is that Ag diffuses through the Ag_2S phase to propagate the film at the sulfur interface. Thus, the rate of this reaction is limited by the time required for the Ag^+ to diffuse, which in turn is inversely proportional to the film thickness. Since $d\alpha/dt$ is inversely proportional to α, integration gives α^2 proportional to time. Apparently, diffusion through the product film is generally possible, so that parabolic laws are most commonly observed. However, in certain cases diffusion occurs so slowly that the film growth is effectively self-stopping. Even in such cases, there is possibility for continued reaction through film breakup followed by reformation and also by mass transport through dislocation or grain boundary defects in the film. For these more complicated cases, a logarithmic law is frequently invoked.

• Supplementary Reading

1. J. P. Hunt, "Metal Ions in Aqueous Solution," Benjamin, New York, 1963.
2. J. O. Edwards, "Inorganic Reaction Mechanisms," Benjamin, New York, 1963.
3. W. M. Latimer, "Oxidation Potentials," 2nd ed., Prentice-Hall, Englewood Cliffs, N.J., 1952.
4. F. Basolo and R. G. Pearson, "Mechanisms of Inorganic Reactions: A Study of Metal Complexes in Solution," Wiley, New York, 1958.
5. N. F. Mott and R. W. Gurney, "Electronic Processes in Ionic Crystals," Clarendon Press, Oxford, 1948.
6. R. P. Bell, "The Proton in Chemistry," Cornell University Press, Ithaca, N.Y., 1959.

Index